Second Edition Revised

ECONOMICS
NEW WAYS OF THINKING

Guided Reading and Study Guide

ROBERT BROWN
California State University San Marcos

EMC Publishing®

ST. PAUL, MINNESOTA

Publisher: Alex Vargas
Managing Editor: Brenda Owens
Production Manager: Bob Dreas
Cover Designer: Leslie Anderson
Design and Production Specialist: Tammy Norstrem

ISBN 978-1-53383-493-5

© by EMC Publishing, LLC
875 Montreal Way
St. Paul, MN 55102
Email: educate@emcp.com
Website: www.emcschool.com

Printed in the United States of America

27 26 25 24 23 22 21 20 19 18   1 2 3 4 5 6 7 8 9 10

CONTENTS

UNIT IV Macroeconomics

Unit V Trade and Investment

INTRODUCTION

Economics is not always easy to understand. Despite all the real-world examples, definitions, graphs, tables, and other support in the *Economics: New Ways of Thinking Student Text*, most students will struggle with at least some economics concepts. The materials in this *Guided Reading and Study Guide* were developed to help students learn and retain the key information presented in their textbook. These materials lead students through the book and give them a variety of opportunities for practice and reinforcement.

This study guide offers an Outlining Activity and a Just the Facts Handout for each section of the textbook. The Outlining Activity provides the major subheads and key ideas of the section, with blanks for students to fill in as they work through or review the section. The Just the Facts Handout summarizes the main ideas of the section in simple, straightforward language.

For each chapter, students will find one or more Graphic Organizer Activities. These display the core content of the chapter in a simple chart form, showing how major ideas are related. Students are asked to engage with this material by filling in blanks in the labels and descriptions.

A Vocabulary Activity presents a list of the key terms from the chapter and a separate list of incomplete definitions. Students are instructed to match each term with its definition by writing the term in the correct blank.

Each chapter also includes a Working with Graphs and Tables Activity. In this exercise, students have an opportunity to supply, manipulate, interpret, or apply information in one or more graphs or tables.

At the end of each chapter is a Practice Test. This test allows students to check their comprehension of the chapter material through a variety of multiple-choice, matching, true-or-false, and short-answer questions.

About the Author

Professor Robert Brown joined the faculty at California State University San Marcos in August 1997. He currently teaches microeconomics, public finance, and environmental and resource economics, as well as the economics of the arts and entertainment industries. His previous teaching experience includes positions at Fullerton High School, the University of North Texas, and the University of California Santa Barbara.

Dr. Brown earned a doctorate in economics from the University of California Santa Barbara in 1991. He received a bachelor's degree in economics from Saint Mary's College of California, and a master's degree in economics from California State University Long Beach.

Dr. Brown's research has appeared in scholarly publications, seminars, and other programs. His topics have included regional land use, valuing environmental resources, urban economics, college athletics, and the economic impacts of health care practices.

CHAPTER 1, SECTION 1
Outlining Activity

Look through the chapter for an overview of the material. Pay attention to the main topics in the book. As you scan each section of the book, fill in the missing words in the following outline.

I. Scarcity Exists

A. People have unlimited _____—things they desire to have.

B. Resources are needed to produce the goods and services that people want.

C. The resources available to satisfy our wants are limited. This condition is called

_____.

II. Scarcity Means Making Choices

A. Scarcity exists because wants are unlimited and resources are limited.

B. Without enough resources to satisfy all of our wants, we must _____

which wants we will satisfy.

III. Making Choices Means Incurring Opportunity Costs

A. Every _____ we make has an opportunity cost.

B. _____ cost is the most valued alternative you give up to do something.

C. A trade-off is another way of thinking about an opportunity cost. A trade-off means that you

can get more of one good only by having less of another good.

IV. One Diagram, Three Economic Concepts

A. A(n) _____ possibilities frontier (PPF) shows all possible combinations of

two goods that an economy can produce in a certain time period. (See Exhibit 1-2 on page 11 of

your textbook.)

B. The PPF tells us that certain things are available to us and certain things are not.

C. The points on the PPF and below it represent what is available to us. The points beyond the PPF

represent what is unavailable to us.

D. The PPF, then, illustrates scarcity by showing us that we can't have everything we want.

E. We must make _____ between combinations of goods along the PPF. For example, in Exhibit 1-2, we can produce 20,000 more sets of skis by choosing point C over point B, but at the opportunity cost of producing 15,000 fewer snowboards.

V. A Consequence of Scarcity: The Need for a Rationing Device

    A. A(n) _____ device is a way to determine who gets what and how much each gets.

    B. _____ (a certain number of dollars) is the most widely used rationing device in our society.

VI. Another Consequence of Scarcity: Competition

    A. Scarcity means people must _____ for resources.

    B. Competition means people try to get more of the rationing device.

VII. A Definition of Economics

    A. Economics is the science that studies the choices of people trying to satisfy their wants in a world of _____.

    B. In other words, economics is the study of how people use their limited _____ to satisfy their unlimited _____.

CHAPTER 1, SECTION 1

Just the Facts Handout

Scarcity Exists

People have **wants**—things they desire to have. Few people are completely satisfied, even after getting their initial wants satisfied. All the wants of all the people in the world make the list of wants unlimited.

Resources are needed to produce the goods and services that satisfy our wants. People's wants are greater than the resources available to satisfy all the wants. This condition is called **scarcity**.

Scarcity Means Making Choices

Wants are unlimited, and resources are limited. Therefore, we must choose how we are going to use our limited resources. We must choose which wants we will try to satisfy and which wants we will leave unsatisfied.

Making Choices Means Incurring Opportunity Costs

The most valued opportunity or alternative you give up to do something is that something's **opportunity cost**. Making choices means that we must make **trade-offs**. The nature of a trade-off is that you can get more of one good only by getting less of another good.

One Diagram, Three Economic Concepts

A **production possibilities frontier** (PPF) shows all possible combinations of two goods that an economy can produce in a certain period of time. (See Exhibit 1-2 on page 11 of your textbook.) The production possibilities frontier can be used to illustrate scarcity, choice, and opportunity cost.

A Consequence of Scarcity: The Need for a Rationing Device

Because scarcity exists, we need a **rationing device**, or a way to decide who gets what portion of all the resources and goods available. Price is the most widely used rationing device in our society. If you are either unwilling or unable to pay the price of something, it won't be yours. By using price, all products are rationed out to the people who are willing and able to pay.

Another Consequence of Scarcity: Competition

Competition exists because of scarcity. Competition takes the form of people trying to get more of the rationing device. If (money or dollar) price is the rationing device, people will compete to earn dollars.

A Definition of Economics

Economics is the science that studies the choices of people trying to satisfy their wants in a world of scarcity. You could say that economics is the study of how people use their limited resources to satisfy their unlimited wants.

Answer questions 1–5 in the Section 1 Assessment on page 13 of your textbook.

CHAPTER 1, SECTION 2
Outlining Activity

Look through the chapter for an overview of the material. Pay attention to the main topics in the book. As you scan each section of the book, fill in the missing words in the following outline.

I. Economic Thinking

   A. Economists see the _____ and opportunity costs in our world.

   B. One objective of this book is to get you to understand and use the economist's way of thinking.

II. Thinking in Terms of Costs and Benefits

   A. There are costs and _____ to almost everything we do.

   B. A person wants to do an activity only if the benefits are greater than the costs.

   C. Weighing the costs and benefits of a problem is what economists call a(n) _____ analysis.

   D. In economics, the word _____ means "additional."

   E. People do not think about the total costs and benefits involved in a decision. Instead, they think about the additional, or marginal, costs and benefits. For example, if you think the marginal (additional) benefits of eating another taco are greater than the marginal costs, then you will buy the additional taco.

III. Thinking in Terms of Incentives

   A. A(n) _____ is something that encourages or motivates a person to take an action. For example, the offer of $10 to mow a lawn is an incentive to do it.

IV. Thinking in Terms of Trade-Offs

   A. We have a trade-off when _____ of one thing means less of something else.

   B. Societies also face trade-offs. For example, if more tax dollars go for education, then fewer tax dollars are available for roads and highways.

V. Thinking in Terms of What Would Have Been

   A. Economists think in terms of "what would have been."

   B. When we can think in terms of "what would have been," then we know the opportunity costs for "what is."

VI. Thinking in Terms of Unintended Effects

A. When things turn out differently from what you intended, your actions have had

_____ effects.

B. Economists think in terms of both unintended effects and _____ effects.

VII. Thinking in Terms of the Small and the Big

A. _____ studies the behavior and choices of relatively small economic units, such as an individual or a single business firm.

B. _____ studies behavior and choices as they relate to the entire economy.

VIII. Thinking in Terms of Theories

A. Economists build _____ to answer economic questions that do not have obvious (easy) answers.

B. A theory is a(n) _____ of how something works, designed to answer a question that has no obvious answer.

C. A theory should be judged by how well it predicts. If theories predict well, then accept them. If theories predict poorly, then do not accept them.

CHAPTER 1, SECTION 2

Just the Facts Handout

Economic Thinking

Learning to understand and use the economist's way of thinking can help you understand the world you live in and may help you get more of what you want in life.

Thinking in Terms of Costs and Benefits

To an economist, almost everything we do involves costs (negatives, disadvantages) and benefits (positives, advantages). Economists think in terms of **marginal**, or additional, costs and benefits rather than total costs and benefits.

Thinking in Terms of Incentives

An **incentive** is something that encourages or motivates a person to take an action.

Thinking in Terms of Trade-Offs

Trade-offs involve opportunity costs. When more of one thing necessarily means less of something else, we have a trade-off. Both individuals and societies face trade-offs. Trade-offs sometimes lead to conflicts in society. For example, one group might want to spend more money on national defense and less money on health and welfare. Another group might prefer the opposite.

Thinking in Terms of What Would Have Been

Economists often think in terms of "what would have been." Thinking in terms of what would have been is important because only then do we know the opportunity costs of "what is."

Thinking in Terms of Unintended Effects

Economists often look for the unintended effects of actions that people take. Has anything ever turned out differently from what you intended? If so, your action had an unintended effect.

Thinking in Terms of the Small and the Big

Microeconomics and *macroeconomics* are the two branches of economics. In **microeconomics**, economists study the behavior and choices of relatively small economic units, such as an individual or a single business firm. In **macroeconomics**, economists study behavior and choices as they relate to the entire economy.

Thinking in Terms of Theories

A theory is a mechanism that an economist uses to answer a question that has no obvious, easy answer. A **theory** offers an explanation of how something works. Economists build theories in order to answer questions that have no obvious answers.

Answer questions 1–5 in the Section 2 Assessment on page 23 of your textbook.

CHAPTER 1, SECTION 3
Outlining Activity

Look through the chapter for an overview of the material. Pay attention to the main topics in the book. As you scan each section of the book, fill in the missing words in the following outline.

I. Goods and Services

   A. Some things people want are tangible and some are _____.

   B. Something is _____ if it can be felt or touched.

   C. A good is anything that satisfies a person's wants. A good brings a person satisfaction, utility, or happiness. A good can be tangible or intangible. A(n) _____ is something that brings a person dissatisfaction, disutility, or unhappiness.

   D. A service is _____. Services are tasks that you pay other people to perform for you.

II. Resources

   A. Resources (also called factors of production) are used to _____ goods and services.

   B. A(n) _____ resource is a resource that can be drawn on indefinitely if it is replaced. For example, wood, or timber, can be "renewed" to maintain a certain supply of it.

   C. A nonrenewable (or exhaustible) resource is a resource that cannot be replenished. For example, oil and natural gas are nonrenewable resources.

   D. The four categories of resources are land, labor, capital, and _____.

   1. Land resources are all the natural resources—such as water, minerals, animals, and forests.

   2. Labor resources are the _____ and mental talents that people contribute to producing goods and services.

   3. Capital refers to produced goods that can be used to _____ other goods. Machines, tools, computers, trucks, buildings, and factories are capital goods.

   4. _____ is the special talent that some people have to develop new business opportunities, new products, and new ways of doing things.

CHAPTER 1, SECTION 3

Just the Facts Handout

Goods and Services

Something is **tangible** if it can be felt or touched. Something is **intangible** if it cannot be felt by touch. A **good** is anything that satisfies a person's wants, that brings a person **utility** (satisfaction or happiness). A good can be either tangible (such as a candy bar) or intangible (such as the feeling of being safe and secure). A bad is something that brings a person **disutility** (dissatisfaction or unhappiness).

  Services are intangible. They are tasks that you pay other people to perform for you. For example, a dentist performs a service for you.

Resources

Resources, or factors of production, are what people use to produce goods and services. A renewable resource can be drawn on indefinitely if it is replaced. A nonrenewable (or exhaustible) resource cannot be replenished.

Land

The resource **land** includes all the natural resources found in nature, such as water, minerals, animals, and forests.

Labor

Labor refers to the physical and mental talents that people contribute to the production of goods and services.

Capital

Capital refers to produced goods that can be used as resources for further production. Such things as machinery, tools, computers, trucks, buildings, and factories are all considered to be capital, or capital goods.

Entrepreneurship

Entrepreneurship refers to the special talent that some people have for searching out and taking advantage of new business opportunities, as well as for developing new products and new ways of doing things.

Answer questions 1–3 in the Section 3 Assessment on page 29 of your textbook.

CHAPTER 1

Graphic Organizer Activity

Supply the missing words in the blank spaces of these graphic organizers.

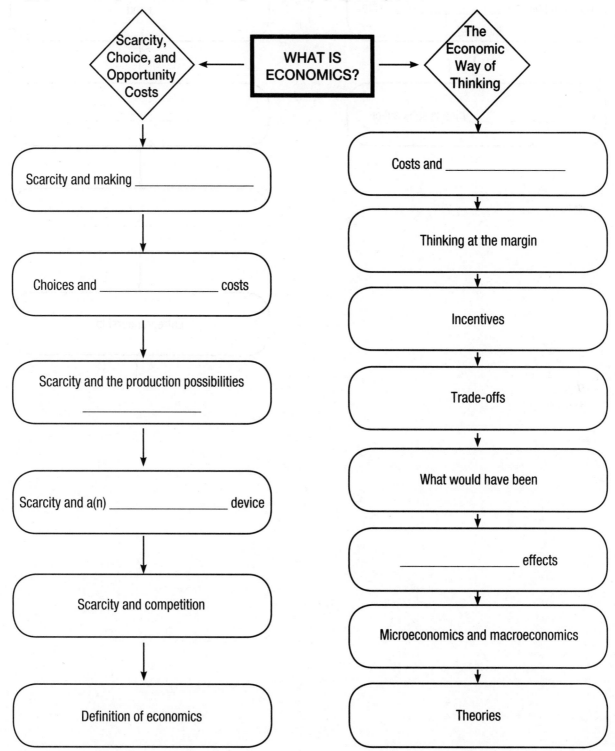

Scarcity, Choice, and Opportunity Costs ← WHAT IS ECONOMICS? → The Economic Way of Thinking

Scarcity and making _____

Choices and _____ costs

Scarcity and the production possibilities _____

Scarcity and a(n) _____ device

Scarcity and competition

Definition of economics

Costs and _____

Thinking at the margin

Incentives

Trade-offs

What would have been

_____ effects

Microeconomics and macroeconomics

Theories

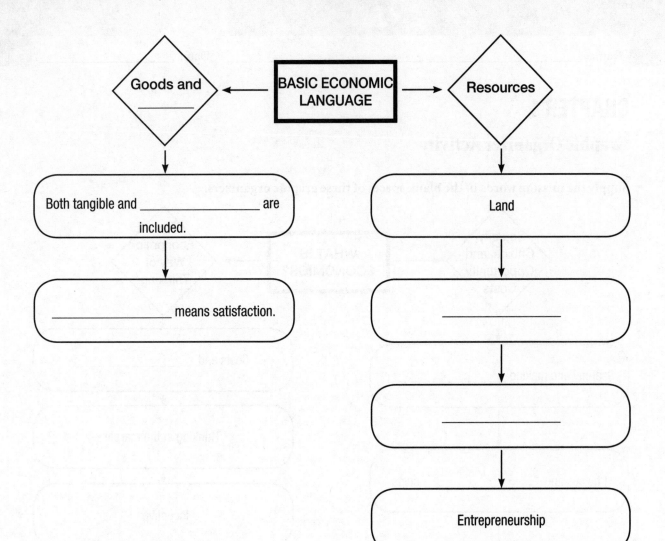

Goods and _____

BASIC ECONOMIC LANGUAGE

Resources

Both tangible and _____ are included.

_____ means satisfaction.

Land

_____

_____

Entrepreneurship

CHAPTER 1
Vocabulary Activity

For each question, fill in the blank with the correct term from the following list.

want	marginal	utility
resource	incentive	disutility
scarcity	microeconomics	services
opportunity cost	macroeconomics	land
trade-off	theory	labor
production possibilities frontier	tangible	capital
rationing device	intangible	entrepreneurship
economics	goods	

1. _____ refers to produced goods that can be used as resources for further production.

2. Something is _____ if it can be felt or touched.

3. In economics, _____ means additional.

4. The special talent that some people have for searching out and taking advantage of new business opportunities and for developing new products and new ways of doing things is referred to as _____.

5. Anything that is used to produce goods or services is a(n) _____.

6. _____ is the quality of bringing satisfaction or happiness.

7. _____ is the condition in which our wants are greater than the resources available to satisfy those wants.

8. _____ focuses on human behavior and choices as they relate to relatively small units—an individual, a business firm, or a single market.

9. An acre of woods, mineral deposits, and water in a stream are all considered _____ resources.

10. An economist uses a(n) _____ to answer a question that has no obvious answer.

11. A graphical representation of all possible combinations of two goods that an economy can produce is a(n) _____.

12. Economists who deal with _____ study behavior and choices as they relate to the entire economy.

13. _____ resources include the physical and mental talents that people contribute to the production of goods and services.

14. The most highly valued opportunity or alternative given up when a choice is made is a(n) _____.

15. _____ are tasks that you pay other people to perform for you.

16. A(n) _____ is a way to decide who gets what and how much of available resources and goods.

17. _____ are anything that satisfies a person's wants or brings satisfaction.

18. A thing that we desire to have is a(n) _____.

19. Something that encourages or motivates a person to take action is a(n) _____.

20. _____ is the quality of bringing dissatisfaction or unhappiness.

21. A situation in which more of one thing necessarily means less of something else is a(n) _____.

22. Something is _____ if it cannot be felt by touch.

23. _____ is the science that studies the choices of people trying to satisfy their wants in a world of scarcity.

Guided Reading and Study Guide

CHAPTER 1

Working with Graphs and Tables Activity

Graphs are often used in economics. Graphs use pictures to compare information. The following bar graph shows the number of home runs hit in a single year for five different players. Use the graph to answer the questions. Write your answers on the lines provided.

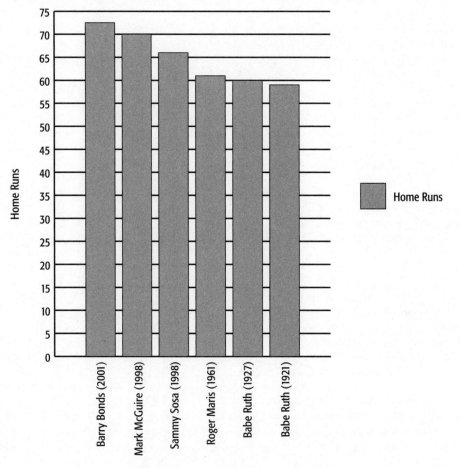

Number of Home Runs Hit in a Single Year

1. How many home runs did Roger Maris hit in 1961?

    _____

2. Who hit more home runs in a single year, Sammy Sosa or Babe Ruth?

    _____

    _____

3. Who hit the most home runs in a single year?

_____

4. How many more home runs did Mark McGuire hit than Roger Maris hit in a single year?

_____

5. Using only the information in the graph, who hit the fewest home runs in a single year?

_____

CHAPTER 1

Practice Test

Multiple Choice

Circle the letter of the correct answer.

1. What is the special talent that some people have for finding new business opportunities and for developing new products and new ways of doing things?

    a. entrepreneurship
    b. incentive
    c. intangible goods
    d. opportunity cost

2. Which of the following is a diagram that shows three economic concepts?

    a. flow chart
    b. bar graph
    c. production possibilities frontier
    d. table

3. Which of the following refers to the physical and mental talents that people contribute to the production of goods and services?

    a. entrepreneurship
    b. labor
    c. capital
    d. land

4. Which of the following encourages a person to take action?

    a. disincentive
    b. interest
    c. incentive
    d. marginal

5. What do economists use to explain how something works and to answer a question that does not have an obvious answer?

    a. labor resources
    b. opportunity costs
    c. marginal thinking
    d. theories

6. Which of the following is a land resource?

    a. iron ore
    b. a forklift
    c. a computer used for bookkeeping
    d. a company salesperson

7. Which of the following is the condition where people's wants are greater than the resources available to satisfy those wants?

    a. opportunity cost
    b. rationing
    c. scarcity
    d. entrepreneurship

8. Because of the existence of scarcity, what must people do?

    a. earn profits
    b. be motivated
    c. make choices
    d. determine wants

9. What determines who gets things and how much they get?

    a. a rationing device
    b. scarcity
    c. opportunity cost
    d. tangible goods

10. What do economists believe that people think about when they make decisions?

    a. incentives
    b. trade-offs
    c. utility
    d. marginal costs and benefits

Matching

For each description, write the letter of the correct category of resource in the blank.

1. _____ A rock band's electric guitar

2. _____ The guitarist in a rock band

3. _____ The field used for your high school soccer team's practice

4. _____ The person who developed the first compact disc

    a. land
    b. entrepreneurship
    c. capital
    d. labor

Short Answer

Write your answers on the lines provided.

1. Why does scarcity mean that people must make choices?

   _____

   _____

2. Why do economists think in terms of costs and benefits?

   _____

   _____

   _____

   _____

   _____

3. Microeconomics and macroeconomics are the two branches of economics. Explain the meanings of microeconomics and macroeconomics.

   _____

   _____

   _____

   _____

4. Many public parks are free to enter. Does this mean that there is no opportunity cost to going to the park? Explain your answer.

   _____

   _____

   _____

   _____

5. Suppose that you decide to go to a baseball game. A ticket to the game costs $5. Also, you must take three hours off from work, and you earn $6 an hour at work. What is the opportunity cost of going to the baseball game?

   _____

   _____

   _____

   _____

CHAPTER 2, SECTION 1

Outlining Activity

Look through the chapter for an overview of the material. Pay attention to the main topics in the book. As you scan each section of the book, fill in the missing words in the following outline.

I. **Three Economic Questions**

   A. What _____ will be produced?

      1. _____ means no country can produce every good it wants in the quantity it would like.

   B. How will the goods be produced?

      1. Will goods be produced by _____?

      2. Will _____ decide how goods are produced?

   C. For whom will the goods be produced?

      1. Will anyone who is able and willing to pay the _____ for the goods be able to obtain them?

      2. Will government decide who will have the goods?

II. **Two Major Economic Systems**

   A. In free enterprise, individuals own most, if not all, the resources and control their use.

   B. In _____, the government controls and may own many of the resources.

III. **Major Differences Between Free Enterprise and Socialism**

   A. In free enterprise, private individuals own resources. In socialism, the _____ owns or controls many of the resources.

   B. In free enterprise, _____ plays a(n) _____ role in the economy. In socialism, government plays a large role in economic decisions.

   C. In socialism, a(n) _____ specifies economic activities. No similar plan exists in free enterprise.

   D. In _____, the government pays little attention to income distribution. In _____, the government is likely to redistribute income.

E. In free enterprise, government does not control _____. In socialism, government decision makers often control _____.

F. Proponents of free enterprise believe that _____ property is sacred. Socialists believe that government should own most of the nonlabor property.

IV. Decentralized Socialism Versus Communism

A. Decentralized Socialism is arguably the _____ form of socialism and communism is a particularly _____ form.

B. There is a greater attempt to take away private property rights under communism than under decentralized socialism.

C. In communism, the _____ comes close to controlling all legal economic activities.

V. Mixed Economies

A. A nation's economic system may contain ingredients of both free enterprise and socialism.

B. Economies that have features of both free enterprise and socialism are called

_____.

VI. The Visions Behind Free Enterprise and Socialism

A. Both free enterprise and socialism are the products of certain visions—ways of looking at, understanding, and explaining the world.

B. The ideas of _____, the eighteenth century economist, are fundamental to free enterprise.

C. The ideas of _____, a nineteenth century economist, are at the heart of socialism (and communism).

D. Smith believed that our self-interest prompts us to work hard, take _____, and in the end, _____ others through our activities.

E. Marx's labor theory of value holds that all value in produced goods is derived from _____. He believed that the owners of factories and business _____ workers by paying them less than they were worth. Marx called the value over and above what the laborer was paid _____ value.

VII. Friedrich Hayek and the Road to Serfdom

A. Friedrich Hayek was an economist known for his book *The Road to Serfdom*.

B. Hayek believed that planning an economy was _____ and only free enterprise allowed for true freedom.

CHAPTER 2, SECTION 1

Just the Facts Handout

Three Economic Questions

All nations must decide how to answer the following three economic questions:
- What goods will be produced?
- How will the goods be produced?
- For whom will the goods be produced?

Two Major Economic Systems

How a society answers the three economic questions defines its **economic system**.

   Free enterprise is an economic system in which individuals own most, if not all, of the resources and control the use of those resources. Sometimes free enterprise is called capitalism or a market economy.

   Socialism is an economic system in which government controls and may own many of the resources. A command economy is a particular type of socialist economic system.

Major Differences Between Free Enterprise and Socialism

Free enterprise and socialism have major differences in the following areas: resources, government's role in the economy, economic plans, income distribution, controlling prices, and private property.

Resources

In free enterprise, resources are owned and controlled by private individuals. In socialism, government controls and may own many of the resources.

Government's Role in the Economy

In free enterprise, government does not decide what goods and services will be produced or how they will be produced. Under socialism, government may make these economic decisions.

Economic Plans

Under socialism, government decision makers may write an **economic plan**. This plan specifies the direction economic activities are to take. A free enterprise economic system would have no such plan.

Income Distribution

Income distribution refers to how all the income earned in a country is divided among different groups of income earners. Less attention is paid to income distribution in free enterprise than in socialism. Government decision makers under socialism are more likely to use government's powers to redistribute income, usually directing it away from society's high earners.

Controlling Prices

In free enterprise, prices are allowed to go up and down. Government does not attempt to control prices. In socialism, government decision makers do control prices, although not all socialist systems control prices to the same extent.

Private Property

Under free enterprise, private property is sacred. The proponents of free enterprise believe that owners of private property are more likely to take care of that property and to use it in its most productive way.

According to socialists, those who own property will end up having more political power. Socialists believe that government should own most nonlabor property, such as factories, raw materials, and machinery. They believe that government will make sure the property is used to benefit the many instead of the few.

Decentralized Socialism Versus Communism

Decentralized socialism and communism are variants of socialism; however, *decentralized socialism* is considered a somewhat weaker form of socialism and *communism* is a particularly strong form. In both, the government owns the nonlabor factors of production. In decentralized socialism, the government oversees much that occurs in the economy but does not control every aspect of the economy (people are freer to decide where they will work and for whom they will work). In communism, by contrast, the government comes close to controlling all legal economic activities. There is a greater attempt to take away private property rights under communism than under decentralized socialism.

Mixed Economies

Mixed economies have features of both free enterprise and socialism. Both the United States and China have mixed economies. However, the United States has much more free enterprise than does China, and China has much more socialism than does the United States. To avoid confusion, economists consider the United States to have a free enterprise economic system, and China to be a socialist nation.

The Visions Behind Free Enterprise and Socialism

Both free enterprise and socialism are the products of certain **visions**—ways of looking at, understanding, and explaining the world. Free enterprise is based on the ideas of Adam Smith, an eighteenth-century economist. Socialism is based on the ideas of Karl Marx, a nineteenth-century economist.

Smith thought that we all desire to make ourselves better off. He believed that our self-interest prompts us to work hard, take risks, and in the end benefit others through our activities. Smith believed that if people want to serve their own self-interest, they have to serve others first.

In contrast, Karl Marx saw self-interest as hurting others. His **labor theory of value** holds that all value in produced goods is derived from labor. Marx believed that in a capitalist society, the owners of factories and businesses exploit the workers by paying them far less than they are worth. Marx used the term **surplus value** to describe the difference between the total value of production and the subsistence wages paid to workers.

Friedrich Hayek and the Road to Serfdom

Friedrich Hayek was an Austrian-born economist and author of *The Road to Serfdom*. Hayek believed that any attempt to plan the economy would fail and that central or government planning led to a kind of dictatorship, where government officials decide—and then dictate—what goods are produced and consumed and who produces what, when, and where. A planned economy, Hayek argued, is an unfree society. For Hayek, socialism was the road to serfdom, and free enterprise was the road to freedom.

Answer questions 1–7 in the Section 1 Assessment on page 42 of your textbook.

CHAPTER 2, SECTION 2
Outlining Activity

Look through the chapter for an overview of the material. Pay attention to the main topics in the book. As you scan each section of the book, fill in the missing words in the following outline.

I. What Is Globalization?

A. Many economists define globalization as a phenomenon by which individuals and businesses in any part of the world are much more _____ by events elsewhere in the world than they used to be.

B. Globalization can also be defined as the growing _____ of the national economies of the world.

C. The first definition of globalization emphasizes that economic agents in any given part of the world are affected by events elsewhere in the _____.

D. Globalization is closely aligned with a movement toward _____.

II. Movement Toward Globalization

A. Early History

    1. The First Era of globalization was from the mid-_____ to the late _____.

    2. The early era of globalization was largely ended by the two world _____ and the _____.

    3. The Cold War divided the world into different camps, which led to relatively high political and economic _____.

B. Recent Causes

    1. The end of the _____ resulted in a thawing of economic relations between former enemies.

    2. Technological innovations lowered transportation or communication _____. Lower _____ mean fewer _____ to trade.

    3. In recent decades, governments of many countries have been _____ their doors to other countries.

III. The Costs and Benefits of Globalization

A. Benefits

    1. Expanding trade extends the benefits of trading to more people.

    2. Trade improves the _____ of people.

B. Costs

    1. Critics often state that globalization has caused _____ income inequality in the world. Supporters of globalization argue that globalization has not caused the increase in income inequality.

    2. Critics of globalization argue that globalization can result in Americans losing jobs due to _____, the practice of hiring people in other countries to do jobs once held by American workers. Supporters of globalization point out that foreign countries around the world _____ jobs to the United States too.

    3. Critics of globalization argue that large, wealthy corporations will decide what will be done in the world instead of governments. Proponents of globalization point out that a government can force people to do certain things that a corporation cannot do.

IV. The Continuing Globalization Debate

A. Globalization doesn't affect everyone in the same way, and often, how it affects you *determines* how you feel about it.

B. The _____ of globalization are more visible than its benefits. People who lose their jobs because of freer international trade know exactly what to blame for their predicament.

V. Globalization and the Financial Crisis

A. Globalization is likely here to stay because people desire to trade.

VI. Three Fallacies About Globalization

A. What matters to the wealth of a country is how much it _____, not how much it exports or imports.

B. All countries can be made better off through globalization and international trade.

C. Workers in some countries receive higher wages than those in other countries because their _____ is higher.

CHAPTER 2, SECTION 2

Just the Facts Handout

What Is Globalization?

Many economists define **globalization** as a process by which events in other parts of the world affect individuals and businesses more and more each day. Globalization can also be defined as the growing integration of the national economies of the world. Some believe that this may lead to a single worldwide economy.

The first definition of globalization emphasizes that economic agents around the world are affected by events elsewhere in the world. In other words, you are affected not only by what happens in the United States but also by what happens in Brazil, Russia, and China. In a sense, globalization makes the world smaller.

Economic globalization is essentially a free enterprise activity, and many countries are moving toward greater free enterprise practices.

Movement Toward Globalization

The world has gone through different globalization periods.

Early History

Globalization has occurred throughout history. For example, it occurred from the mid-1800s to the late-1920s. World War I, World War II, and the Great Depression largely ended this early era of globalization. After the Depression, globalization stopped because the Cold War led to relatively high political and economic barriers.

Recent Causes

Several factors have led to the period of globalization that began in the 1990s.

- The end of the Cold War brought about less political and economic tension between the capitalist and communist worlds. Political and economic relations improved, and one giant barrier to trade was no longer there.
- Advancing technology (which lowered transportation and communication costs) helped to overcome the trade barrier of physical distance.
- Policy changes by governments in recent decades have allowed for increased trade.

The Costs and Benefits of Globalization

Some people argue that the benefits of globalization outweigh the costs. Other people take the opposite view.

Benefits

People who favor globalization include trade and a higher standard of living as its major benefits.

- The process of globalization really means that people are trading with more people, at greater distances. So, the benefits of trade are extended to more people.
- Trade improves people's standard of living. For example, as both India and China opened up their economies to globalization in recent decades, they experienced increases in income per person.

Costs

People who oppose globalization include increased inequality of incomes, loss of American jobs, and more power to big corporations as its major costs.

- Globalization's critics often point out that globalization seems to increase income inequality between rich and poor countries. The supporters of globalization argue that, while increased income inequality and globalization seem to go together, there is no evidence that globalization *causes* income inequality.

- Many critics of globalization argue that globalization results in Americans losing certain jobs due to **offshoring**, which is the practice of hiring people in other countries to do jobs once held by American workers. Supporters of globalization point out that offshoring is a two-way street. Foreign countries around the world offshore jobs to the United States, too.

- Many critics of globalization argue that the process will simply "turn over" the world to large, Western corporations. Instead of governments deciding what will and will not be done, large corporations will decide. The proponents of globalization point out that a government can force people to do certain things (such as pay taxes or join the military) while a corporation cannot. Supporters also argue that critics overestimate the influence of international corporations.

The Continuing Globalization Debate

To a large degree, whether one supports or criticizes globalization seems to depend on where "one is sitting." Globalization doesn't affect everyone in the same way, and often, how it affects *you* determines how you feel about it.

The benefits of globalization are often difficult to see. For example, the supporters of globalization argue that it brings greater economic wealth, lower prices (than would otherwise exist), more innovation, less poverty, and so on. Yet, sometimes it is difficult for us to see all these benefits.

The costs of globalization are more visible. People who lose their jobs because of freer international trade in the world know exactly what to blame for their predicament. As consumers, these people surely could receive some benefits from globalization. But as workers, they also could incur some rather high costs. They are likely to know of the costs but be unaware of the benefits.

Globalization and the Financial Crisis

Some argue that the financial crisis has placed a damper on globalization forces. Adam Smith believed that the inclination to trade sets us apart from other species. The desire to trade will probably not diminish.

Three Fallacies About Globalization

Inaccurate information and assumptions about globalization exist. One fallacy is that a country is always better off if it exports many goods and imports very few goods; however, what really matters to the wealth of a country is how much it produces, *not* how much it exports or imports.

Many people believe that with globalization, some countries will be made better off economically and others will be made worse off; but this is not the case. All countries can be made better off through globalization. Consider the fact that at the heart of globalization is international trade.

Another belief is that in a globalized world, business will gravitate toward the countries where wages are low, but this belief overlooks the fact that workers in some countries receive higher wages than those in other countries because their productivity is higher.

Answer questions 1–4 in the Section 2 Assessment on page 55 of your textbook.

Name: _____ Date: _____

CHAPTER 2

Graphic Organizer Activity

Supply the missing words in the blank spaces of these graphic organizers.

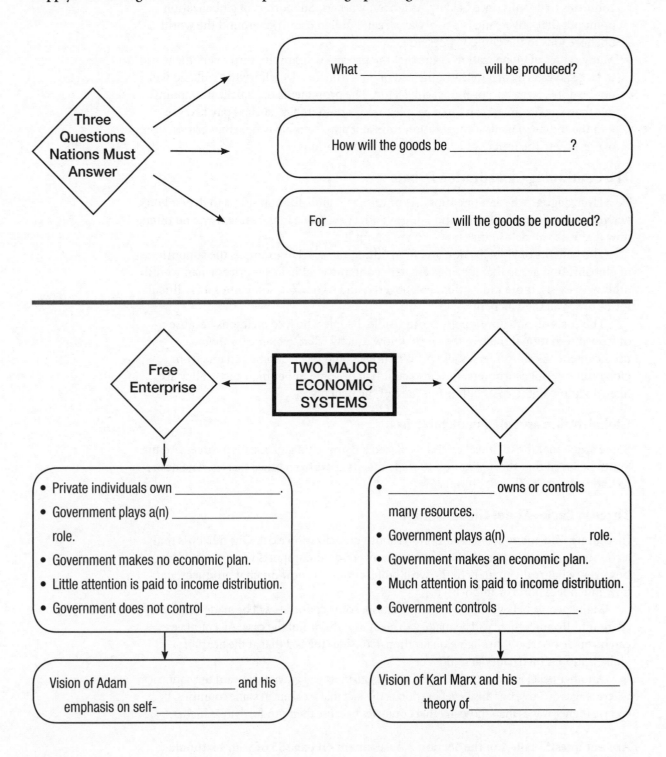

Three Questions Nations Must Answer

What _____ will be produced?

How will the goods be _____?

For _____ will the goods be produced?

TWO MAJOR ECONOMIC SYSTEMS

Free Enterprise

_____

- Private individuals own _____.
- Government plays a(n) _____ role.
- Government makes no economic plan.
- Little attention is paid to income distribution.
- Government does not control _____.

- _____ owns or controls many resources.
- Government plays a(n) _____ role.
- Government makes an economic plan.
- Much attention is paid to income distribution.
- Government controls _____.

Vision of Adam _____ and his emphasis on self-_____

Vision of Karl Marx and his _____ theory of_____

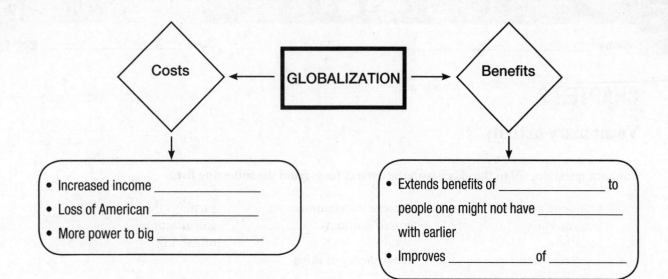

- Increased income _____
- Loss of American _____
- More power to big _____

- Extends benefits of _____ to people one might not have _____ with earlier
- Improves _____ of _____

CHAPTER 2

Vocabulary Activity

For each question, fill in the blank with the correct term from the following list.

economic system	income distribution	surplus value
free enterprise	mixed economy	globalization
socialism	vision	offshoring
economic plan	labor theory of value	

1. Many economists define _____ as a phenomenon by which individuals and businesses in any part of the world are affected by events elsewhere in the world.

2. In Marxist terminology, _____ is the difference between the total value of production and the subsistence wages that are paid to workers.

3. The _____ holds that all value in produced goods is derived from labor.

4. The way in which a society decides what goods to produce, how to produce them, and for whom goods will be produced is its _____.

5. An economy that has some elements of both capitalism and socialism is a(n) _____.

6. _____ is the term used to describe work done for a company by persons other than the original company's employees in a country other than the one in which the company is located.

7. _____ is an economic system in which government controls and may own many of the resources.

8. _____ is the way all the income in a country is divided among different groups of income earners.

9. _____ is a sense of how the world works.

10. _____ is an economic system in which individuals own most, if not all, the resources and control their use.

11. A government program specifying economic activities, such as what goods will be produced and what prices will be charged, is a(n) _____.

CHAPTER 2

Working with Graphs and Tables Activity

The following table illustrates the major differences between socialist thinkers and capitalist thinkers. In the lines provided, explain these differences in the areas listed.

Socialism	Free enterprise
Prices	
Private property	
Role of government	
Early thinkers and their works	Early thinkers and their works

CHAPTER 2

Practice Test

Multiple Choice

Circle the letter of the correct answer.

1. Which of the following promoted the idea that people always have the desire to make themselves better off?

    a. Karl Marx
    b. International Monetary Fund
    c. Adam Smith
    d. Thomas Friedman

2. Which of the following is not true about globalization?

    a. In order for globalization to work, some countries must be made worse.
    b. Some workers receive higher wages than those in other countries because their productivity is higher.
    c. A country's wealth in a globalized world is based on how much it produces, not on how much it imports or exports.
    d. The benefits of globalization include an improved standard of living.

3. Which of the following is a free enterprise belief?

    a. Prices should be allowed to fluctuate.
    b. Resources should be rationed by government.
    c. Mixed economies exploit consumers.
    d. Prices should be controlled by government.

4. Which of the following terms is used to describe work done for a company by people other than the original employees in a country other than the one in which the company is located?

    a. socialism
    b. offshoring
    c. free enterprise
    d. self-interest

5. According to Marx, what is the difference between the total value of production and the subsistence wages paid to workers?

    a. surplus value
    b. wealth
    c. value of labor
    d. slavery

6. Which of the following is *not* one of the three economic questions all nations must decide how to answer?

    a. How will goods be produced?
    b. For whom will goods be produced?
    c. What goods will be produced?
    d. What wages will workers be paid?

7. Which of the following is often viewed as a cost of globalization?

    a. more trade
    b. higher standard of living
    c. gains in American jobs
    d. more power to big companies

8. Which of the following is viewed as a recent cause for movement toward more globalization?

    a. the end of the Cold War
    b. greater income inequality
    c. greater availability of world resources
    d. socialism

True or False

For each of these statements, place a T in the blank if the statement is true or an F if the statement is false.

1. _____ The United States is considered a pure free enterprise nation because it has no features of socialism.

2. _____ A socialist thinker believes that private property ends up in the hands of a few people who have a lot of power.

3. _____ A capitalist thinker believes that government works in the best interest of the public as a whole.

4. _____ Immediately after World War II, the process of globalization increased.

5. _____ The Internet increases the probability that people will trade with each other.

Short Answer

Write your answers on the lines provided.

1. What is the difference between free enterprise and socialism in the area of income distribution?

    _____

    _____

    _____

    _____

    _____

    _____

2. According to Adam Smith, is self-interest good or bad for society? Explain your answer.

    _____

    _____

    _____

    _____

    _____

3. How has globalization made the world "smaller" today than it was 100 years ago?

    _____

    _____

    _____

    _____

    _____

    _____

4. Why is globalization likely to be here to stay?

    _____

    _____

    _____

    _____

    _____

    _____

Guided Reading and Study Guide

CHAPTER 3, SECTION 1
Outlining Activity

Look through the chapter for an overview of the material. Pay attention to the main topics in the book. As you scan each section of the book, fill in the missing words in the following outline.

I. How Does Free Enterprise Answer the Three Economic Questions?

    A. _____ will produce the goods that consumers want to buy.

    B. The individuals who _____ and _____ the business firms decide how goods will be produced.

    C. Goods are produced for those people who are _____ and _____ to buy them.

II. Five Features of Free Enterprise

    A. _____

    B. Choice (or Freedom to Choose)

    C. Voluntary Exchange

    D. _____

    E. Economic Incentives

III. Laws, Institutions, and Regulations

    A. A country's _____ system determines, to a large degree, how free enterprise operates.

    B. Legal systems and institutions can either help or hinder free enterprise.

IV. The Circular Flow

    A. The circular flow of economic activity in the U.S. economy shows the relationships among the key players in the economy. (See Exhibit 3-2 on page 66 of your textbook.)

    B. _____ sell resources to businesses, and businesses pay for these resources.

    C. _____ sell goods and services to households, and households pay for these goods and services.

    D. Households pay taxes to _____, and _____ provides goods and services to households.

    E. Businesses pay taxes to government, and government provides goods and services to businesses.

CHAPTER 3, SECTION 1

Just the Facts Handout

How Does Free Enterprise Answer the Three Economic Questions?

A free enterprise economy answers the three economic questions as follows:

1. **What goods will be produced?** Business firms will produce the goods that consumers want to buy.
2. **How will these goods be produced?** The individuals who own and manage the business firms decide how goods will be produced.
3. **For whom will the goods be produced?** Goods are produced for people who are willing and able to buy them. A person who has both willingness to buy and the ability to buy pays a price for the good or service.

Five Features of Free Enterprise

Five major features or characteristics define free enterprise: private property, choice, voluntary exchange, competition, and economic incentives.

Private Property

Any good that is owned by an individual or a business—such as a car, a house, a factory, or a piece of machinery—is **private property**. Any good that is owned by the government—such as the Statue of Liberty—is **public property**.

   Under free enterprise, individuals and businesses have the right to own property. Furthermore, they may own as much property as they are willing and able to purchase, and they may sell whatever property they own.

Choice (or Freedom to Choose)

Workers have the right to choose the work they will do and for whom they will work. Businesses have the right to choose the products they will produce and offer for sale. Buyers have the right to choose the products they will buy.

Voluntary Exchange

Individuals have the right to make the exchanges or trades that they believe will make them better off. Individuals make themselves better off by trading what they value less for what they value more.

Competition

Individuals are free to compete with others.

Economic Incentives

Money acts as an incentive to produce. If you produce goods and services that people are willing and able to buy, you receive money in return.

Laws, Institutions, and Regulations

Free enterprise operates in a country in which there are certain laws, institutions, and regulations. Legal systems and institutions can either interfere with free enterprise or encourage free enterprise.

The Circular Flow

A **circular flow of economic activity** shows the economic relationships that exist between different economic groups in an economy. Exhibit 3-2 on page 66 of your textbook shows the key players in the U.S. economy, the relationships they have with each other, and the ways they interact. The key players in the U.S. economy are businesses, government, and households. A **household** is an economic unit of one person or more that sells resources and buys goods and services.

The relationships between the different economic agents are as follows:

- Households sell resources to businesses, and businesses pay for those resources.
- Businesses sell goods and services to households, and households pay for those goods and services.
- Households pay taxes to the government, and the government provides goods and services to households.
- Businesses pay taxes to the government, and the government provides goods and services to businesses.

The circular flow diagram allows us to see how a change in one thing in the economy will lead to a change somewhere else in the economy. For example, a change in taxes will lead to a change in the amount households spend on goods and services produced by businesses.

Answer questions 1–8 in the Section 8 Assessment on page 67 of your textbook.

CHAPTER 3, SECTION 2

Outlining Activity

Look through the chapter for an overview of the material. Pay attention to the main topics in the book. As you scan each section of the book, fill in the missing words in the following outline.

I. Profits and Losses

A. **Profit** is the amount of money left over after all costs have been paid. Profit equals total

_____ (price of a good times the units of the good sold) minus total

_____ (average cost of a good times the number of units of the good sold).

B. A loss occurs when total cost is greater than total revenue.

II. Profit and Loss as "Signals"

A. Profits and losses are signals to the firms earning the profits or taking the losses.

B. Profits and losses in firms are signals to other firms. Firms enter an industry when there are profits to be earned and exit when there are losses.

C. Resources flow _____ profit. Resources flow _____ from losses.

CHAPTER 3, SECTION 2

Just the Facts Handout

Profits and Losses

Profit is the amount of money left over after all the costs of production have been paid. Profit can also be described in terms of total revenue and total cost.

Total revenue is the price of a good multiplied by the number of units of the good sold. Total cost is the average cost of a good multiplied by the number of units of the good sold. When total revenue is greater than total cost, a firm earns a profit.

When total cost is greater than total revenue, a loss occurs. A **loss** is the amount of money by which total cost exceeds total revenue.

Profit and Loss As "Signals"

Profits and losses are signals to the firms earning the profits or taking the losses. If a firm is earning a profit, it continues to produce its product. If a firm is taking a loss, it will likely discontinue its product or reduce production of the product.

Profits and losses are also seen as signals to others in the industry. Profits attract firms to enter the industry. Losses encourage firms to exit the industry.

Answer questions 1–5 in the Section 2 Assessment on page 71 of your textbook.

CHAPTER 3, SECTION 3
Outlining Activity

Look through the chapter for an overview of the material. Pay attention to the main topics in the book. As you scan each section of the book, fill in the missing words in the following outline.

I. Ethics and Free Enterprise

    A. An ethical economic system should have four characteristics. Supporters of free enterprise say that the free enterprise economic system has these characteristics.

        1. Allow individuals to _____ their own occupations or professions.

        2. Produce the goods and services preferred by both the majority and the _____.

        3. _____ (or _____) producers according to how well (or poorly) they respond to the preferences of the buying public.

        4. Provide people with numerous freedoms, including the freedom to work where they want to work, the freedom to start their own businesses if they want, the freedom to acquire property, the freedom to buy and sell the goods they want to buy and sell, and even the freedom to fail.

II. Economic _____ in Key Documents

    A. The Bill of Rights shows a high regard for private property.

    B. The Declaration of Independence encourages free _____—an essential ingredient of free enterprise—with the rest of the world.

    C. The Constitution preserves competition—an important feature of free enterprise—by denying states the right to tax each other's goods.

III. Economic Rights and Responsibilities in a Free Enterprise Economy

    A. The right to voluntary exchange comes with the responsibility to give the other person accurate _____ about what is being exchanged.

    B. The right to private property comes with the responsibility of using one's property only for _____ purposes.

    C. People have a responsibility to compete in a truthful, legitimate manner.

CHAPTER 3, SECTION 3

Just the Facts Handout

Ethics and Free Enterprise

Ethics consists of the principles of conduct, such as right and wrong, morality and immorality, good and bad. The free enterprise system needs to have certain characteristics or qualities to be considered an ethical system.

People Can Choose

An ethical economic system allows individuals to choose their own occupations or professions. Supporters of free enterprise state that free enterprise has this characteristic.

A Variety of Products

An ethical economic system produces the goods and services preferred by both the majority and the minority. Supporters of free enterprise state that free enterprise responds to both the majority and minorities.

Rewards Depend on Performance

An ethical economic system rewards (or punishes) producers according to how well (or poorly) they respond to the preferences of the buying public. Supporters of free enterprise state that it fits this description.

Numerous Freedoms

Proponents of free enterprise argue that no economic system can be ethical if it limits people's freedom. In free enterprise, they say, people have numerous freedoms: the freedom to work where they want to work, the freedom to start their own businesses if they want, the freedom to acquire property, the freedom to buy and sell the goods they want to buy and sell, and even the freedom to fail.

Economic Principles in Key Documents

The Constitution, the Bill of Rights, and the Declaration of Independence have a special significance to free enterprise: each document contains principles of free enterprise.

Bill of Rights

The Bill of Rights states that "private property [shall not] be taken for public use, without just compensation." This statement shows a high regard for private property.

Declaration of Independence

The signers of the Declaration of Independence listed many complaints against the king of Great Britain, George III. One complaint was that the king had prevented the 13 colonies from "trad[ing] with all parts of the world." This statement emphasizes both freedom of choice and voluntary exchange—essential ingredients of free enterprise.

The Constitution

The U.S. Constitution favors preserving competition. Article 1, Section 8, says that "no tax or duty shall be laid on articles exported from any State." If states had been allowed to tax each other's goods, competition within each state would have been lessened.

Economic Rights and Responsibilities in a Free Enterprise Economy

Along with certain rights in a free enterprise economy, people have responsibilities.

Open Disclosure

The right to voluntary exchange comes with the responsibility of giving the other person accurate information about what is being exchanged.

Obeying the Law

The responsibility associated with the right to private property is the responsibility of using one's property only for legal purposes. It is a responsibility to respect and abide by the law.

Being Truthful

The economic right to compete in a free enterprise system comes with the responsibility to compete in a truthful, legitimate manner.

Answer questions 1–4 in the Section 3 Assessment on page 76 of your textbook.

CHAPTER 3, SECTION 4

Outlining Activity

Look through the chapter for an overview of the material. Pay attention to the main topics in the book. As you scan each section of the book, fill in the missing words in the following outline.

   I. Imagine Being an Entrepreneur

      A. An entrepreneur searches out and takes advantage of new business opportunities.

      B. An entrepreneur develops new _____.

      C. An entrepreneur develops new ways of doing things.

      D. The public benefits from entrepreneurs taking _____.

   II. Entrepreneurs, Profit, and Risk

      A. Entrepreneurs take risks so they can earn a(n) _____.

      B. Many entrepreneurs risk their time and _____ and end up with nothing.

CHAPTER 3, SECTION 4

Just the Facts Handout

Imagine Being an Entrepreneur

An **entrepreneur** is a person who has a special talent for searching out new business opportunities and taking advantage of them. Most people, when faced with the task of finding a new business opportunity, end up scratching their heads. Most people are not entrepreneurs. Entrepreneurs are a tiny minority of the population.

If an entrepreneur succeeds in coming up with an idea for a new product, develops and produces it, and then offers it for sale, we are made better off. Entrepreneurs play an important role in society by taking risks to develop new products or new ways of doing things that benefit the public. From a consumer's point of view, having more risk-taking entrepreneurs in a society likely means having more choices of goods and services in that society.

Entrepreneurs, Profit, and Risk

Entrepreneurs are willing to risk their time and money to try to develop new products and to change products because they hope to earn a high profit. If laws limited entrepreneurs' profits, fewer people would be willing to become entrepreneurs. As it is, many entrepreneurs risk their time and money and end up with nothing.

Answer questions 1–3 in the Section 4 Assessment on page 79 of your textbook.

CHAPTER 3, SECTION 5

Outlining Activity

Look through the chapter for an overview of the material. Pay attention to the main topics in the book. As you scan each section of the book, fill in the missing words in the following outline.

I. Government as _____ of Contracts

   A. A contract is an agreement between two or more people to do something.

   B. Government _____ people who break their contracts. In other words, the government enforces contracts.

   C. Without government to enforce contracts, the risk of going into business would be too great for many people.

II. Government as Provider of Nonexcludable _____ Goods

   A. If one person's consumption of a good does *not* _____ another person from consuming the same good, then the good is a public good.

   B. A free enterprise economy will produce private goods and excludable public goods. A free enterprise economy will not produce _____ goods.

   C. _____ are people who receive the benefits of a good without paying for it.

   D. Many economists believe that the government should provide nonexcludable public goods.

   E. One way for people to communicate what nonexcludable public goods they want is through the _____ process.

III. Externalities

   A. An action by someone that has an adverse side effect on someone else is a negative _____, or a negative third-party effect.

   B. An action by someone that has a beneficial side effect on someone else is a positive _____, or a positive third-party effect.

   C. Some people argue that government should subsidize those activities that generate positive externalities for society at large.

   D. Some people argue that it is government's duty to reduce negative externalities. Government can do so through the court system, _____, and _____.

CHAPTER 3, SECTION 5

Just the Facts Handout

Government as Enforcer of Contracts

A **contract** is an agreement between two or more people to do something. A society needs some institution to enforce contracts. In our society, government can punish people who break their contracts.

Government as Provider of Nonexcludable Public Goods

Goods are categorized as private goods or public goods. A **private good** is a good of which one person's consumption takes away from another person's consumption. A **public good** is a good of which one person's consumption does not take away from another person's consumption.

All public goods are not the same. An **excludable public good** is a public good that individuals can be physically prohibited from consuming. A **nonexcludable public good** is a public good that individuals cannot be physically prohibited from consuming.

Excludable Public Goods

Movies in theaters are excludable public goods because theater owners can (and do) prevent people from watching the movies. If you go to a theater and refuse to pay the ticket price, then the theater owner will probably not permit you to enter. The owner will exclude you from viewing the movie.

Nonexcludable Public Goods

People cannot be prevented from consuming a nonexcludable public good. For example, the national defense of the United States is a public good because one person's consumption of it does not prevent another person's consumption. It is a nonexcludable public good because the U.S. government cannot exclude anyone in the United States from consuming its national defense. It is physically impossible, or prohibitively costly, not to protect everyone. If an enemy's missiles are headed for the United States and the U.S. government destroys the incoming missiles, it protects all the people in the country.

Who Will Produce Nonexcludable Public Goods?

Economists contend that in a free enterprise economy, people will be willing to produce private goods and excludable public goods, but no one will want to produce nonexcludable public goods. This is because once a nonexcludable public good is produced, no one will pay for it. People will not pay for something they cannot be excluded from consuming. Economists call people who receive the benefits of a good without paying for it **free riders**.

The Political Process

A free enterprise economy will not produce nonexcludable public goods. Many economists argue that the government should provide nonexcludable public goods. In the U.S. system of government, people can use the political process to communicate what nonexcludable public goods they want and how much of these goods they want.

Externalities

A **negative externality** is an adverse side effect of an act that is felt by others. A **positive externality** is a beneficial side effect of an action that is felt by others.

Government and Positive Externalities

Education generates positive externalities. As a student, you not only learn things that will directly help you in life and in the workplace, but also become a better citizen and a more informed voter. Becoming a better citizen and a more informed voter ends up benefiting more people than just you. Education at public schools is not directly paid for by the people who receive it. Instead, it is subsidized by taxpayers. Some people argue that government should use tax money to subsidize all the activities that generate positive externalities for society.

Government and Negative Externalities

Some people argue that government should minimize the "bad" in society. In other words, government should reduce the occurrence of negative externalities. Government can do so in three principal ways: through the court system, regulation, and taxation.

Answer questions 1–5 in the Section 5 Assessment on page 87 of your textbook.

CHAPTER 3

Graphic Organizer Activity

Supply the missing words in the blank spaces of these graphic organizers.

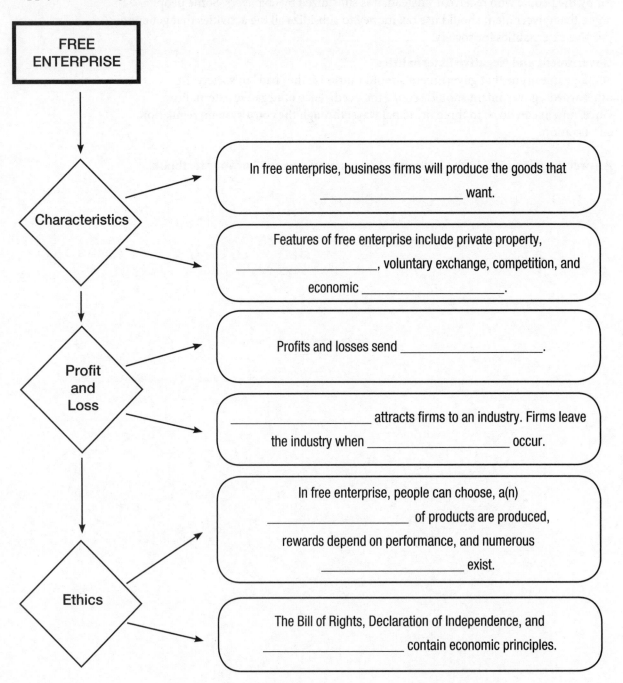

FREE ENTERPRISE

Characteristics

In free enterprise, business firms will produce the goods that _____ want.

Features of free enterprise include private property, _____, voluntary exchange, competition, and economic _____.

Profit and Loss

Profits and losses send _____.

_____ attracts firms to an industry. Firms leave the industry when _____ occur.

Ethics

In free enterprise, people can choose, a(n) _____ of products are produced, rewards depend on performance, and numerous _____ exist.

The Bill of Rights, Declaration of Independence, and _____ contain economic principles.

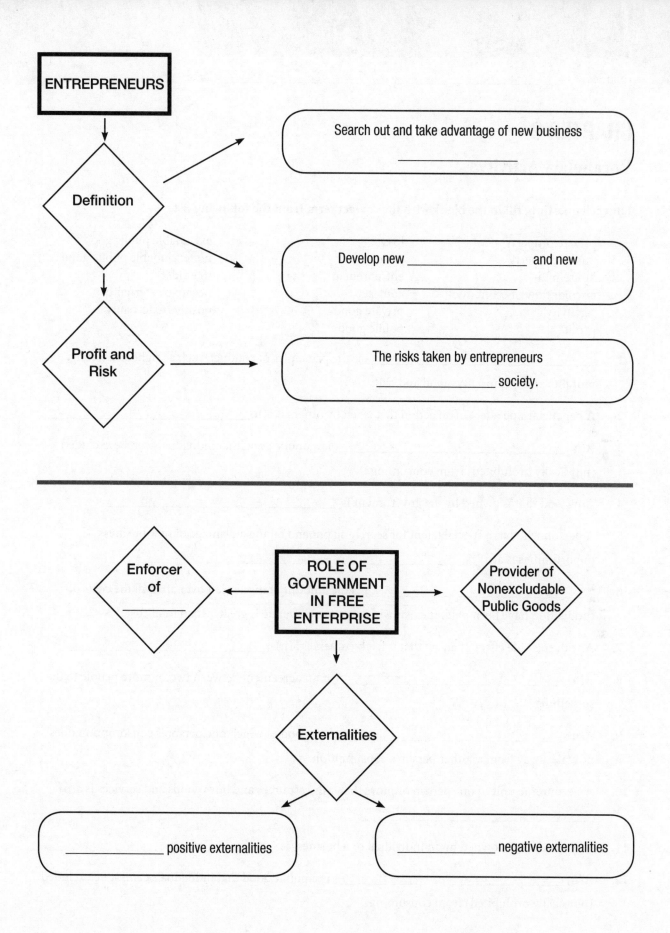

ENTREPRENEURS

Definition

Search out and take advantage of new business
_____

Develop new _____ and new
_____

Profit and Risk

The risks taken by entrepreneurs
_____ society.

Enforcer of
_____

ROLE OF GOVERNMENT IN FREE ENTERPRISE

Provider of Nonexcludable Public Goods

Externalities

_____ positive externalities

_____ negative externalities

CHAPTER 3
Vocabulary Activity

For each question, fill in the blank with the correct term from the following list.

private property   loss   excludable public good
public property   ethics   nonexcludable public good
household   entrepreneur   free rider
circular flow of economic   contract   negative externality
   activity   private good   positive externality
profit   public good

1. _____ is the principles of conduct, such as right and wrong, morality and immorality, good and bad.

2. A beneficial side effect of an action that is felt by others is a(n) _____.

3. A(n) _____ is a public good that individuals can be excluded (physically prohibited) from consuming.

4. Any good that is owned by the government is _____.

5. A person who has a special talent for searching out and taking advantage of new business opportunities is a(n) _____.

6. _____ is the amount of money left over after all the costs of production have been paid. It exists whenever total revenue is greater than total cost.

7. An adverse side effect of an act that is felt by others is a(n) _____.

8. A(n) _____ is an agreement between two or more people to do something.

9. A(n) _____ is a good of which one person's consumption does not take away from another person's consumption.

10. An economic unit of one person or more that sells resources and buys goods and services is a(n) _____.

11. Any good that is owned by an individual or a business is _____.

12. A(n) _____ is a public good that individuals cannot be excluded (physically prohibited) from consuming.

13. A good of which one person's consumption takes away from another person's consumption is a(n) _____.

14. _____ is the amount of money by which total cost exceeds total revenue.

15. A(n) _____ is a person who receives the benefits of a good without paying for it.

16. The economic relationships that exist between different economic groups in an economy is the _____.

CHAPTER 3

Working with Graphs and Tables Activity

Use the equations on page 68 of the student text to complete the following table for a small business that makes snowboards.

Price540$60	Quantity produced and sold	Average cost	Total cost	Profit
$30	20	$25	_____	$100
$20	25	_____	$500	$0
$15	35	$10	$350	$175
$12	40	_____	$440	_____
$10	_____	$9	$	

CHAPTER 3

Practice Test

Multiple Choice

Circle the letter of the correct answer.

1. According to supporters of free enterprise, which of the following should the government do?

    a. enforce contracts
    b. provide private goods
    c. subsidize negative externalities
    d. own all of society's resources

2. For which of the following goods does one person's consumption not take away from another person's consumption?

    a. private good
    b. excludable good
    c. public good
    d. resource good

3. Which of the following is any good that is owned by an individual or a business?

    a. private property
    b. public property
    c. positive property
    d. free rider property

4. Which of the following is *not* a characteristic of an ethical economic system?

    a. freedom to fail
    b. guaranteed profits
    c. production of a variety of goods
    d. rewards for performance

5. In economics, a free rider is which of the following?

    a. someone who rides in a friend's car without paying for gas
    b. someone who does not charge a price for selling a product
    c. someone who works for free
    d. someone who receives the benefits of a good without paying for it

6. What does a firm's total profit equal?

    a. average cost minus total revenue
    b. price minus total cost
    c. total revenue minus total cost
    d. total cost minus average cost

Matching

For each description, write the letter of the correct feature of free enterprise in the blank.

1. _____ You now work for XYZ computer software company, and another company offers you a job.

2. _____ A friend offers you $5 for a CD that you do not listen to anymore. You decide to make the trade with her.

3. _____ You own a car.

4. _____ High earnings by lawyers attract people to the law profession.

5. _____ You and a friend discuss whether to eat lunch at a fast-food burger restaurant or a sandwich shop.

6. _____ Sellers try to attract more customers by offering lower prices.

    a. private property
    b. choice (or freedom to choose)
    c. voluntary exchange
    d. competition
    e. economic incentives

True or False

For each of these statements, place a T in the blank if the statement is true or an F if the statement is false.

1. _____ In free enterprise, the government should enforce contracts and punish people who break their contracts.

2. _____ People in a free enterprise economy are willing to produce and offer to sell nonexcludable public goods.

3. _____ The circular flow of economic activity shows profit or loss in an economy.

4. _____ Many entrepreneurs do not risk time and money to develop a new product.

5. _____ Government can use the court system, regulation, and taxation to reduce negative externalities in society.

Short Answer

Write your answers on the lines provided.

1. Do you think you would work harder on homework assignments if they were not graded? Explain why or why not using concepts from this chapter.

   _____

   _____

   _____

2. Jo owns a gas station in Ponder, Texas. Last year, Jo sold 5,000 gallons of gasoline at a price of $4 a gallon. Jo's average cost of producing the 5,000 gallons of gasoline was $2 a gallon. Did Jo earn a profit? If so, how much?

    _____

    _____

3. Upon graduating from college, you receive several job offers. Explain how competition in free enterprise benefits you in this situation.

    _____

    _____

    _____

CHAPTER 4, SECTION 1

Outlining Activity

Look through the chapter for an overview of the material. Pay attention to the main topics in the book. As you scan each section of the book, fill in the missing words in the following outline.

I. What Is Demand?

    A. Markets are where people come together to buy and sell goods or services.

        1. _____ is the buying side of a market.

        2. _____ is the selling side of a market.

    B. Demand refers to the *willingness and ability* of buyers to purchase a good or service.

II. What Does the Law of Demand "Say"?

    A. The law of demand says that as the price of a good _____, quantity demanded of the good _____, and as price of a good decreases, quantity demanded of the good increases.

    B. *Quantity* _____ refers to the number of units of a good purchased at a specific price.

III. Why Do Price and Quantity Demanded Move in Opposite Directions?

    A. Price and quantity demanded move in opposite directions because of the law of diminishing marginal utility.

    B. The law of diminishing marginal utility states that as a person consumes additional units of a good, the utility gained from each additional unit of the good _____.

IV. The Law of Demand in Numbers and Pictures

    A. A demand _____ is a numerical chart showing the law of demand.

    B. A demand curve is a(n) _____ representation of the law of demand.

V. Individual Demand Curves and Market Demand Curves

    A. A(n) _____ demand curve represents an individual's demand.

    B. A(n) _____ demand curve is the sum of all individual demand curves added together.

CHAPTER 4, SECTION 1

Just the Facts Handout

What Is Demand?

A **market** is a place where people buy and sell things. A market has two sides. There is a buying side and a selling side. The buying side of a market is called *demand*. The selling side is called *supply*.

Demand is the willingness and ability of buyers to purchase different amounts of something at different prices, during a specific time period. Willingness to buy means a person has a desire for a product. Ability means a person has the money to pay for it. Without both willingness and ability, there is no demand. Both must be present for there to be demand.

What Does the Law of Demand "Say"?

The **law of demand** says that when the price of a product goes up, the quantity demanded goes down. This law also says the opposite. It says that when the price goes down, the quantity demanded goes up.

Quantity demanded refers to the number of units of a good that are purchased at a specific price. Notice that the terms *demand* and *quantity demanded* sound alike. They are, however, different. You will learn more about this later.

Why Do Price and Quantity Demanded Move in Opposite Directions?

The **law of diminishing marginal utility** says that as a person uses more of a product, the person gets less satisfaction from it. For example, you get less satisfaction from the second hamburger you eat than from the first. You get less satisfaction from the third than from the second. And so on.

The law of diminishing marginal utility affects the law of demand. The more satisfaction you receive from something, the more you will pay. The less satisfaction you receive, the less you will pay. This means that you will buy more of something only if it costs less. This is the law of demand.

The Law of Demand in Numbers and Pictures

We can show the law of demand with both numbers and pictures. A **demand schedule** shows the law of demand with numbers. A **demand curve** shows the law of demand in picture form (graphically). (See Exhibit 4-1 on page 101 of your textbook.)

Individual Demand Curves and Market Demand Curves

An individual demand curve shows one person's demand for a good. A market demand curve shows the sum of all the individual curves for the good. (See Exhibit 4-2 on page 102 of your text.)

Answer questions 1–4 in the Section 1 Assessment on page 103 of your textbook.

CHAPTER 4, SECTION 2

Outlining Activity

Look through the chapter for an overview of the material. Pay attention to the main topics in the book. As you scan each section of the book, fill in the missing words in the following outline.

   I. When Demand Changes, the Curve Shifts

      A. A rightward shift means that demand has _____.

      B. A leftward shift means that demand has _____.

  II. What Factors Cause Demand Curves to Shift?

      A. Income

         1. A good for which demand rises as income rises and falls as income falls is a(n) _____.

         2. A good for which demand falls as income rises and rises as income falls is a(n) _____ good.

         3. If a person buys the same amount of a good when income changes, the good is a neutral good.

      B. Buyer_____

         1. People's _____ affect how much of a good they buy.

      C. Prices of Related Goods

         1. With _____, the demand for one good moves in the same direction as the price of the other good.

         2. With _____, the demand for one good moves in the opposite direction as the price of the other.

      D. Number of _____

         1. The more buyers, the higher the demand; the fewer buyers, the lower the demand.

      E. _____ Price

         1. Buyers who expect the price of a good to be _____ in the future may buy the good now. In this case, current demand for the good _____.

         2. Buyers who expect the price of a good to be _____ in the future may wait and buy the good later. In this case, current demand for the good falls.

III. What Factor Causes a Change in Quantity Demanded?

B. Only the _____ of the good can directly cause a change in the

_____.

A. A change in quantity demanded refers to a movement _____ a demand

curve.

CHAPTER 4, SECTION 2

Just the Facts Handout

When Demand Changes, the Curve Shifts

Demand can change. It can go up, or it can go down.

When demand changes, the demand curve moves. It can move either left or right. When demand increases, the curve moves to the right. When demand decreases, the curve moves to the left. (See Exhibit 4-3 on page 105 of your textbook.)

What Factors Cause Demand Curves to Shift?

Several things can cause demand to change. These factors include
- income;
- buyer preferences;
- prices of related goods;
- number of buyers; and
- future price.

Income

When a person's income changes, his or her demand for goods can change. The changes in demand depend on the goods involved.

Economists talk about three kinds of goods when they talk about income and demand:
- normal goods
- inferior goods
- neutral goods

If income and demand move in the same direction, the good is a **normal good**. For example, if your income rises and you buy more of a good, the good is a normal good. If your income falls and you buy less, the good is also a normal good.

If income and demand move in opposite directions, the good is an **inferior good**. If your income goes up and you buy less of a good, it is an inferior good. If your income goes down and you buy more, the good is also an inferior good.

If income changes but the demand does not change, the good is a **neutral good**.

Buyer Preferences

People's preferences (what they like most) affect demand. If more people start to like something, demand goes up for that item. If demand goes up, the demand curve moves to the right. If people stop liking something, the demand goes down and the curve shifts to the left.

Prices of Related Goods

Demand is affected by the prices of related goods. There are two types of related goods. These are substitutes and complements.

Substitutes are similar goods. One can take the place of the other. Peanuts can substitute for pretzels, for example. The price of one good and the demand for the other move in the same direction. For example, if the price of pretzels goes up, the demand for peanuts goes up.

Complements are two goods that are used together. Tennis rackets and tennis balls are complements. The demand for one good and the price of the other move in opposite directions. If the price of tennis rackets goes up, the demand for tennis balls goes down.

Guided Reading and Study Guide

Number of Buyers

The more buyers for a good, the higher the demand. The fewer buyers, the lower the demand.

Future Price

Buyers may expect the price of a good to be higher in the future. If so, they may buy now. This increases the current demand. The opposite can also happen. Buyers might think the price will be lower in the future. In this case, they may wait to buy. This decreases the current demand.

What Factor Causes a Change in Quantity Demanded?

Only one factor can change quantity demanded. This factor is price. The change is shown as movement *along* a demand curve. (See Exhibit 4-4[b] on page 109 of your text.)

Answer questions 1–3 in the Section 2 Assessment on page 109 of your textbook.

CHAPTER 4, SECTION 3

Outlining Activity

Look through the chapter for an overview of the material. Pay attention to the main topics in the book. As you scan each section of the book, fill in the missing words in the following outline.

I. What Is Elasticity of Demand?

A. Elasticity of demand deals with the relationship between price and quantity demanded.

B. Elasticity of demand compares the percentage change in _____ with the percentage change in _____.

C. Elasticity of demand is seen as the following ratio:

$$\text{Elasticity of demand} = \frac{\text{Percentage change in quantity demanded}}{\text{Percentage change in price}}$$

D. _____ demand exists when the quantity demanded (the numerator) changes by a greater percentage than the percentage change in price (the denominator).

E. _____ demand exists when the quantity demanded (the numerator) changes by a smaller percentage than the percentage change in price (the denominator).

F. _____ demand exists when the quantity demanded (the numerator) changes by the same percentage as the percentage change in price (the denominator).

II. What Determines Elasticity of Demand?

A. Number of Substitutes

B. _____ Versus Necessities

C. Percentage of _____ Spent on the Good

D. Time

III. An Important Relationship Between Elasticity and Total Revenue

A. Case 1: Elastic demand and a price increase cause total revenue to _____.

B. Case 2: Elastic demand and a price decrease cause total revenue to _____.

C. Case 3: Inelastic demand and a price increase cause total revenue to _____.

D. Case 4: Inelastic demand and a price decrease cause total revenue to _____.

CHAPTER 4, SECTION 3
Just the Facts Handout

What Is Elasticity of Demand?

Elasticity of demand deals with the relationship between price and quantity demanded. It measures the impact of a price change. A small price change can cause a big change in how many of a certain product people buy. Or a small price change can cause little change in the number of units of a good that people buy.

How do economists measure the relationship between price and quantity demanded? They compare the percentage change in price with the percentage change in quantity demanded. They do this by dividing the percentage change in quantity demanded by the percentage change in price. This comparison produces three types of results:
- When the percentage change in quantity demanded is greater than the percentage change in price, the result is **elastic demand**.
- When the percentage change in quantity demanded is less than the percentage change in price, the result is **inelastic demand**.
- When the percentage change in quantity demanded is the same as the percentage change in price, the result is **unit-elastic demand**.

What Determines Elasticity of Demand?

Four factors affect elasticity of demand:
- number of substitutes
- whether the good is a luxury or a necessity
- percentage of income spent on the good
- time

Number of Substitutes

Some goods have few substitutes. Other goods have many. Heart medicine is an example of a good with few substitutes. A soft drink is an example of a good with many substitutes.

If a good has few substitutes, the demand will probably be inelastic. If a good has many substitutes, the demand will probably be elastic.

Luxuries Versus Necessities

Necessary goods are goods that people feel they need to survive. Food is a necessary good. Even if the price increases, people will not be able to cut back on these goods. The demand for necessities tends to be inelastic.

Luxuries are goods that people do not need to survive. Very expensive cars are luxuries. If the price increases, people will cut back on their purchases of these items. The demand for luxuries tends to be elastic.

Percentage of Income Spent on the Good

Buyers react more to price changes on goods for which they spend a lot of their income. The demand for these goods tends to be elastic. On the other hand, buyers don't react much to price changes if they spend a small amount of their income on a good. The demand for such a good tends to be inelastic.

Time

More time means more chances to change how much people buy after a price change. With more time, they can find substitutes. They can change their lifestyle. This means their demand is more elastic with more time.

With little time to react, people tend not to change the amount they buy after a price change. They do not have time to react, so their demand tends not to change. This means the demand is inelastic.

An Important Relationship Between Elasticity and Total Revenue

Whether demand for a good is elastic or inelastic matters to sellers of goods. It affects their total revenue. Four different results can occur when prices rise or fall:

- If demand is elastic, an increase in price causes a decline in total revenue.
- If demand is elastic, a decrease in price causes an increase in total revenue.
- If demand is inelastic, an increase in price causes an increase in total revenue.
- If demand is inelastic, a decrease in price causes a decrease in total revenue.

Answer questions 1–4 of the Section 3 Assessment on page 119 of your textbook.

CHAPTER 4

Graphic Organizer Activity

Supply the missing words in the blank spaces of this graphic organizer.

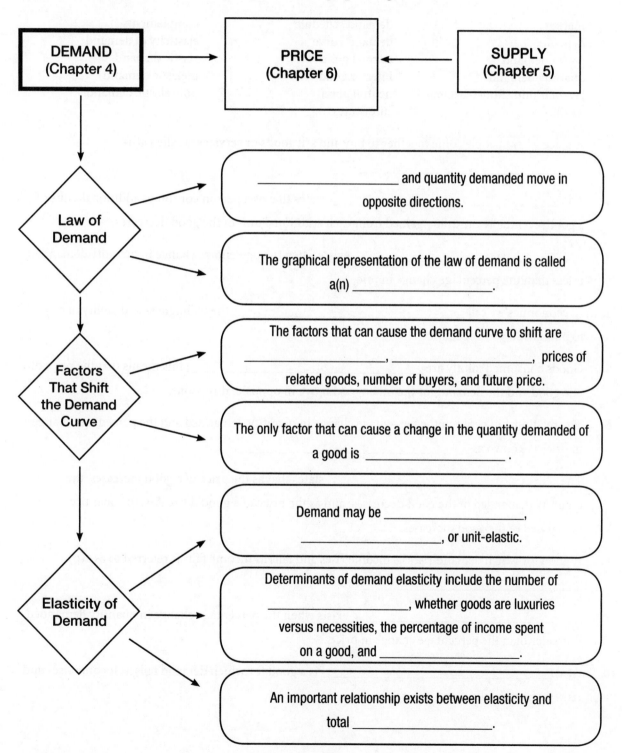

| DEMAND (Chapter 4) | → | PRICE (Chapter 6) | ← | SUPPLY (Chapter 5) |

Law of Demand

_____ and quantity demanded move in opposite directions.

The graphical representation of the law of demand is called a(n) _____.

Factors That Shift the Demand Curve

The factors that can cause the demand curve to shift are _____, _____, prices of related goods, number of buyers, and future price.

The only factor that can cause a change in the quantity demanded of a good is _____ .

Elasticity of Demand

Demand may be _____, _____, or unit-elastic.

Determinants of demand elasticity include the number of _____, whether goods are luxuries versus necessities, the percentage of income spent on a good, and _____.

An important relationship exists between elasticity and total _____.

CHAPTER 4

Vocabulary Activity

For each question, fill in the blank with the correct term from the following list.

market   demand schedule   complements
demand   demand curve   elasticity of demand
law of demand   normal good   elastic demand
quantity demanded   inferior good   inelastic demand
law of diminishing marginal   neutral good   unit-elastic demand
  utility   substitutes

1. A place where people come together to buy and sell goods or services is called a(n)
    _____.

2. The _____ states that as a person consumes additional units of
    a good, eventually the utility gained from each additional unit of the good decreases.

3. _____ exists when the percentage change in quantity demanded
    is less than the percentage change in price.

4. In economics we call _____ the willingness and ability of buyers
    to purchase a good or service.

5. Goods consumed jointly are _____; this means that the price of
    one good and the demand for the other good move in opposite directions.

6. The relationship between the percentage change in quantity demanded and the percentage change
    in price is known as _____.

7. The _____ states that as the price of a good increases, the
    quantity demanded of the good decreases, and as the price of a good decreases, the quantity
    demanded of the good increases.

8. A good for which demand rises as income rises and falls as income falls is referred to as a(n)
    _____.

9. _____ exists when the percentage change in quantity demanded
    is greater than the percentage change in price.

10. A(n) _____ is a good for which demand falls as income rises and
    rises as income falls.

Guided Reading and Study Guide   © EMC Publishing

11. A good for which demand remains unchanged as income rises or falls is called a(n)
_____.

12. Two goods are _____ if the price of one good and the demand for the other move in the same direction.

13. _____ exists when the percentage change in quantity demanded is the same as the percentage change in price.

14. _____ refers to the number of units of a good purchased at a specific price.

15. A numerical chart showing the law of demand is called a(n) _____.

16. A(n) _____ is a line that represents the law of demand on a graph.

Name: _____   Date: _____

CHAPTER 4

Working with Graphs and Tables Activity

The exhibit below shows a demand curve for tickets to Beyonce concerts. Each of the following occurrences causes a shift in the demand curve. For each occurrence, draw a new demand curve that shows how the demand curve shifts. Label each demand curve with the appropriate number. The first one (labeled D_1) is completed for you.

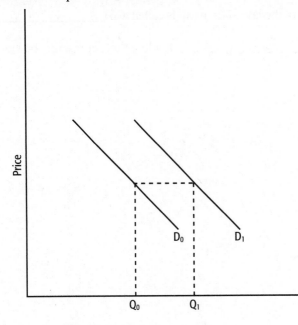

Quantity of Tickets Demanded

1. Concert promoters begin a huge advertising pitch for the concerts.

2. Beyonce releases a new hit song.

3. The incomes of concert fans decrease (assume concerts are normal goods).

4. Shakira (a substitute for Beyonce) hits the road with a concert tour.

CHAPTER 4

Practice Test

True or False

For each of these statements, place a T in the blank if the statement is true or an F if the statement is false.

1. _____ Suppose that the demand for football tickets at your school is elastic. If your school lowers the price of tickets, then total revenue from ticket sales will increase.

2. _____ The price of DVDs increases 10 percent and the quantity demanded of DVDs falls 5 percent. The demand for DVDs is elastic.

3. _____ According to the law of demand, as the price of a good increases, the quantity demanded of the good decreases.

4. _____ Peanut butter and jelly are complement goods. If the price of jelly increases, then the demand for peanut butter increases.

5. _____ The law of diminishing marginal utility states that as a person consumes additional units of a good, eventually the utility gained from each additional unit of the good increases.

6. _____ If the percentage change in price is 10 percent and the percentage change in quantity demanded is 5 percent, then the elasticity of demand is equal to 2.

7. _____ If the price of concert tickets increases, the demand for concert tickets will decrease.

8. _____ A demand curve graphically shows the law of demand.

9. _____ If Joe's demand for hot dogs falls as his income rises, then hot dogs are an inferior good.

10. _____ A good will tend to have a more elastic demand if it has many substitutes.

11. _____ A person who has a long period of time to adjust to price increases in housing will likely have an elastic demand for housing.

Short Answer

Write your answers on the lines provided.

1. Suppose that the number of students in your high school decreases by a large amount next year. What will likely happen to the demand for sodas at your school vending machines?

   _____

   _____

2. The basketball team at your school is having an especially good season. Are there more or fewer people at their basketball games this year? Explain your answer, using the concept of demand.

   _____

   _____

3. Explain the difference between a change in demand and a change in quantity demanded.

_____

_____

4. Shirley has a job at Burger Delight. Her boss recently increased the price of burgers. The boss tells Shirley that after the price increase, revenues at Burger Delight went down. If you were Shirley, how would you explain this to the boss? In your answer, use the concepts of demand and elasticity.

_____

_____

_____

Guided Reading and Study Guide

CHAPTER 5, SECTION 1
Outlining Activity

Look through the chapter for an overview of the material. Pay attention to the main topics in the book. As you scan each section of the book, fill in the missing words in the following outline.

I. What Is Supply?

    A. Supply refers to the willingness and _____ of sellers to produce and offer to sell a good.

II. What Does the Law of Supply Say?

    A. The law of supply says that as the price of a good _____, the quantity supplied of the good _____, and as the price of a good decreases, the quantity supplied of the good decreases.

    B. Price and quantity supplied move in the same direction, or have a(n) _____.

    C. _____ refers to the number of units of a good produced and offered for sale at a specific price.

III. The Law of Supply in Numbers and Pictures

    A. A supply _____ is a numerical chart showing the law of supply.

    B. A supply _____ is a graphical representation of the law of supply.

IV. A Vertical Supply Curve

    A. The law of supply does not hold for goods that can no longer be produced. The supply curve for this type of good is _____.

    B. The law of supply does not hold when there is no time to produce more of a good. The supply curve for this type of good is vertical.

V. A Firm's Supply Curve and a Market Supply Curve

    A. A(n) _____ supply curve is the supply curve for a particular firm.

    B. A(n) _____ supply curve is the sum of all firms' supply curves.

CHAPTER 5, SECTION 1
Just the Facts Handout

What Is Supply?

Supply is the willingness and ability of sellers to produce and sell different quantities of a good at different prices during a specific time period. Willingness to produce and sell means that the person wants to produce and sell the good. Ability to produce and sell means that the person is capable of producing and selling the good.

What Does the Law of Supply Say?

The **law of supply** says that as the price of a good increases, the quantity supplied of the good increases, and as the price of a good decreases, the quantity supplied of the good decreases. Price and quantity supplied have a **direct relationship** because they move in the same direction.

    Quantity supplied refers to the number of units of a good produced and offered for sale at a specific price. Notice that supply and quantity supplied do not mean the same thing.

The Law of Supply in Numbers and Pictures

A **supply schedule** shows the law of supply in numbers. A **supply curve** shows the law of supply in pictures (graphically). (See Exhibit 5-1 on page 126 of your textbook.)

    A supply curve shows the amount of a good that sellers are willing and able to sell at various prices.

A Vertical Supply Curve

The law of supply does not hold true for all goods. It also does not hold true over all time periods. Some goods, such as Stradivarius violins, can no longer be produced. So supply cannot be increased. The supply curve for Stradivarius violins is vertical.

    For other goods, there is no time to produce more of the good. If a theater is sold out for tonight's play, the supply of seats cannot be increased in time for the performance. The supply curve of theater seats for tonight's performance is vertical.

A Firm's Supply Curve and a Market Supply Curve

A firm's supply curve is the supply curve for a particular firm. A market supply curve is the sum of all firms' supply curves. (See Exhibit 5-3 on page 127 of your textbook.)

Answer questions 1–5 in the Section 1 Assessment on page 127 of your textbook.

CHAPTER 5, SECTION 2

Outlining Activity

Look through the chapter for an overview of the material. Pay attention to the main topics in the book. As you scan each section of the book, fill in the missing words in the following outline.

I. When Supply Changes, the Curve Shifts

   A. A rightward shift means supply has _____.

   B. A leftward shift means supply has _____.

II. What Factors Cause Supply Curves to Shift?

   A. Resource Prices

      1. A decrease in a resource price increases supply. The supply curve shifts to the

      _____.

      2. An increase in a resource price decreases supply. The supply curve shifts to the

      _____.

   B. Technology

      1. An advancement in technology increases supply. The supply curve shifts to the right.

   C. Taxes

      1. A(n) _____ in taxes decreases supply. The supply curve shifts
      to the left.

      2. If a tax is _____, the supply curve will shift back to the right.

   D. Subsidies

      1. An increase in subsidies increases supply. The supply curve shifts to the right.

      2. If a subsidy is _____, the supply curve will shift back to the left.

   E. Quotas

      1. A quota _____ supply. The supply curve shifts to the left.

      2. If a(n) _____ is eliminated, the supply curve will shift back to the right.

F. Number of Sellers

    1. An increase in the number of sellers increases supply, and the supply curve shifts to the right.

    2. A decrease in the number of sellers decreases supply, and the supply curve shifts to the left.

G. Future _____

H. Weather (in Some Cases)

    1. Bad weather may decrease the supply of some agricultural products. Unusually good weather can increase supply.

    2. Bad weather, such as hurricanes, can also affect the supply of nonagricultural products.

III. What Factor Causes a Change in Quantity Supplied?

    A. The only factor that can cause a change in the quantity supplied of a good is a change in the _____ of the good.

    B. A change in _____ supplied is shown as a movement along a given supply curve.

IV. Elasticity of Supply

    A. Elasticity of supply is the relationship between the percentage change in quantity supplied and the percentage change in _____.

    B. Elasticity of supply can be written as the following ratio:

$$\text{Elasticity of supply} = \frac{\text{Percentage change in quantity supplied}}{\text{Percentage change in price}}$$

        1. _____ supply exists when the percentage change in quantity supplied (the numerator) is greater than the percentage change in price (the denominator).

        2. _____ supply exists when the percentage change in quantity supplied (the numerator) is less than the percentage change in price (the denominator).

        3. _____ supply exists when the percentage change in quantity supplied (the numerator) is the same as the percentage change in price (the denominator).

CHAPTER 5, SECTION 2

Just the Facts Handout

When Supply Changes, the Curve Shifts

Supply can go up, and it can go down. When the supply of a good changes, the supply curve for that good shifts, or moves. The supply curve moves to the right if supply goes up, and it moves to the left if supply goes down.

What Factors Cause Supply Curves to Shift?

Supply curves shift because of changes in several factors. These factors include
- resource prices;
- technology;
- taxes;
- subsidies;
- quotas;
- number of sellers;
- future price; and
- weather.

Resource Prices

Resources (land, labor, capital, and entrepreneurship) are used to produce goods and services. When resource prices fall, sellers are willing and able to produce and sell more of the good. The supply curve shifts to the right.

When resource prices rise, sellers are willing and able to produce and sell less of the good. The supply curve shifts to the left.

Technology

Technology is the skills and knowledge used in production. An **advancement in technology** is the ability to produce more output with a fixed amount of resources. So, an advancement in technology lowers the **per-unit cost**, or average cost of a good. Suppliers are willing and able to produce and offer to sell more output at lower per-unit costs. The supply curve shifts to the right.

Taxes

Some taxes increase per-unit costs. This "extra cost" of doing business causes a supplier to supply less output. The supply curve shifts to the left. If the tax is eliminated, the supply curve will shift back to its original position.

Subsidies

A **subsidy** is a payment made by government to certain suppliers. A subsidy shifts the supply curve to the right. If the subsidy is removed, the supply curve will shift back to its original position.

Quotas

A **quota** is a legal limit on the number of units of a foreign-produced good (import) that can enter a country. A quota decreases supply, so the supply curve shifts to the left. The elimination of a quota causes the supply curve to shift back to its original position.

Number of Sellers

If more sellers begin producing a particular good, supply increases, and the supply curve shifts to the right. If some sellers stop producing a particular good, supply decreases, and the supply curve shifts to the left.

Future Price

If sellers expect the price of a good to be higher in the future, they may hold back the good now and supply it in the future. If sellers expect the price of a good to be lower in the future, they may want to supply the good now instead of in the future.

Weather (in Some Cases)

Bad weather can reduce the supply of many agricultural goods, such as corn, wheat, and barley. Unusually good weather can increase the supply. Bad weather, such as hurricanes, can affect the supply of other goods, such as those produced in coastal areas.

What Factor Causes a Change in Quantity Supplied?

The price of a good is the *only* factor that can cause a change in the quantity supplied of the good. A change in the price of a good causes a movement along the good's supply curve.

Elasticity of Supply

Elasticity of supply is the relationship between the percentage change in quantity supplied and the percentage change in price. Elasticity of supply can be written as a ratio: the percentage change in quantity supplied divided by the percentage change in price.

Elastic supply exists when the percentage change in quantity supplied is greater than the percentage change in price (when the numerator in the ratio changes by more than the denominator).

Inelastic supply exists when the percentage change in quantity supplied is less than the percentage change in price (when the numerator in the ratio changes by less than the denominator).

Unit-elastic supply exists when the percentage change in quantity supplied is the same as the percentage change in price (when the numerator in the ratio changes by the same percentage as the denominator).

Answer questions 1–5 in the Section 2 Assessment on page 137 of your textbook.

CHAPTER 5

Graphic Organizer Activity

Supply the missing words in the blank spaces of this graphic organizer.

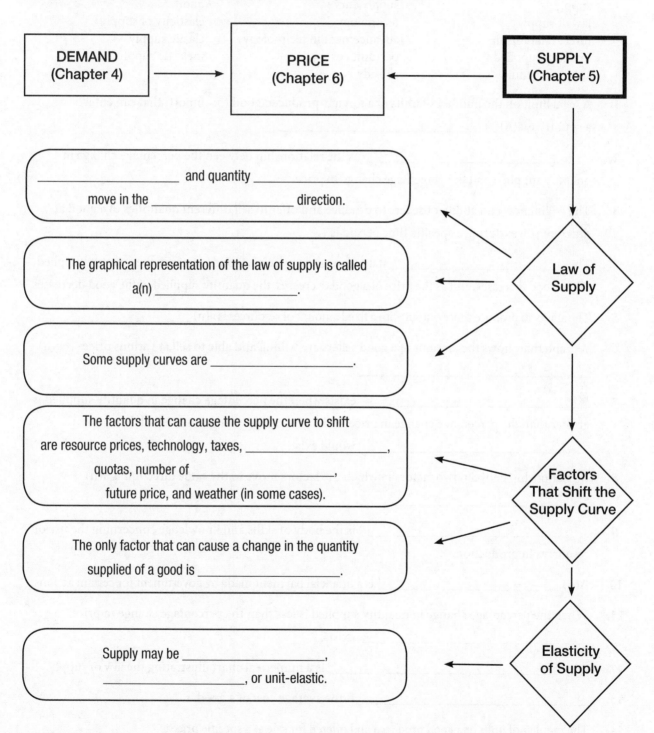

DEMAND
(Chapter 4)

PRICE
(Chapter 6)

SUPPLY
(Chapter 5)

_____ and quantity _____ move in the _____ direction.

The graphical representation of the law of supply is called a(n) _____.

Some supply curves are _____.

The factors that can cause the supply curve to shift are resource prices, technology, taxes, _____, quotas, number of _____, future price, and weather (in some cases).

The only factor that can cause a change in the quantity supplied of a good is _____.

Supply may be _____, _____, or unit-elastic.

Law of Supply

Factors That Shift the Supply Curve

Elasticity of Supply

CHAPTER 5

Vocabulary Activity

For each question, fill in the blank with the correct term from the following list.

supply	supply curve	quota
law of supply	technology	elasticity of supply
direct relationship	advancement in technology	elastic supply
quantity supplied	per-unit cost	inelastic supply
supply schedule	subsidy	

1. A legal limit on the number of units of a foreign-produced good (or import) that can enter a country is a(n) _____.

2. _____ is the relationship between the percentage change in quantity supplied and the percentage change in price.

3. The willingness and ability of sellers to produce and offer to sell different quantities of a good at different prices during a specific time period is _____.

4. The _____ states that as the price of a good increases, the quantity supplied of the good increases, and as the price of a good decreases, the quantity supplied of the good decreases.

5. The ability to produce more output with a fixed amount of resources is a(n) _____.

6. A graph that shows the amount of a good sellers are willing and able to sell at various prices is a(n) _____.

7. _____ exists when the percentage change in quantity supplied is greater than the percentage change in price. If the percentage change were equal then _____ would exist.

8. A relationship between two factors in which the factors move in the same direction is a(n) _____.

9. _____ is the body of skills and knowledge concerning the use of resources in production.

10. A(n) _____ is a financial payment made by government for certain actions.

11. When the percentage change in quantity supplied is less than the percentage change in price, _____ exists.

12. A(n) _____ is a numerical chart illustrating the law of supply.

13. _____ is the average cost of a good.

14. The number of units of a good produced and offered for sale at a specific price is _____.

CHAPTER 5

Working with Graphs and Tables Activity

The exhibit below shows a supply curve for DVDs. Each of the following occurrences causes a shift in the supply curve. For each occurrence, draw a new supply curve that shows how the supply curve shifts. Label each supply curve with the appropriate number. The first one (labeled S_1) is completed for you.

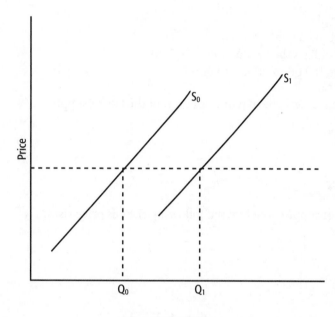

Quantity of DVDs

1. An advancement of technology allows more DVDs to be produced with a fixed amount of resources.

2. A tax is imposed on each DVD produced and sold.

3. The price of the plastic used to make DVDs increases.

4. New firms enter the DVD industry and start to sell DVDs over the Internet.

CHAPTER 5

Practice Test

Multiple Choice

Circle the letter of the correct answer.

1. Which of the following changes will cause the supply curve to shift to the left?

   a. resource prices fall
   b. an advancement in technology occurs
   c. government subsidizes the production of a good
   d. a tax is placed on the production of a good

2. Which of the following is a graphical representation of the law of supply?

   a. quantity supplied
   b. inelastic supply
   c. supply curve
   d. supply schedule

3. According to the law of supply, which of the following rises as price rises?

   a. supply
   b. demand
   c. price of resources
   d. none of the above

4. The percentage change in the quantity supplied of baseball games equals the percentage change in the price of baseball tickets. Which of the following is true about the supply of baseball games?

   a. The supply of baseball games is elastic.
   b. The supply of baseball games is inelastic.
   c. The supply of baseball games is unit-elastic.
   d. None of the above is true.

5. Which of the following will increase the supply of outdoor concerts?

   a. The price of renting outdoor stadiums for concerts decreases.
   b. Many cities restrict the number of concerts allowed each year.
   c. A tax is placed on outdoor concert events.
   d. Unusually bad weather occurs in the areas of the concerts.

6. The price of this textbook rises 10 percent and the quantity supplied of the book rises 14 percent. Which of the following is true about the supply of this textbook?

   a. The supply of this textbook is elastic.
   b. The supply of this textbook is inelastic.
   c. The supply of this textbook is unit-elastic.
   d. None of the above is true.

7. Gas to drive to and from school each week (five round trips) costs $20. What is the average cost per day for gas to drive back and forth to school?

   a. $10
   b. $20
   c. $4
   d. $5

8. What is a legal limit on the number of units of a foreign-produced good (or import) that can enter a country called?

   a. a subsidy
   b. an elastic good
   c. a tariff
   d. a quota

9. Which of the following describes the supply curve of baseballs hit for home runs during the 1999 World Series?

   a. The supply curve is vertical.
   b. The supply curve is horizontal.
   c. The supply curve slopes upward from left to right.
   d. The supply curve slopes downward from left to right.

10. Which of the following will shift the supply curve for a good to the right?

   a. an increase in the price of a resource
   b. an advancement in technology
   c. an increase in a tax on the good
   d. a decrease in the number of sellers

Short Answer

Write your answers on the lines provided.

1. Suppose that high schools started paying money to students who play soccer. What do you think would happen to the number of players competing in high school soccer? According to the law of supply, would you expect to see more, fewer, or the same number of students wanting to play high school soccer?

   _____

   _____

   _____

2. Explain the difference between a change in supply and a change in quantity supplied in terms of the supply curve.

   _____

   _____

3. A recent series of cold winter storms froze much of the citrus crop in California. According to the law of supply, explain how this bad weather will change the supply of citrus.

   _____

4. When Matt earned $8 an hour, he chose to work 10 hours a week at his job at a grocery store. Then, his boss raised his pay to $9 an hour. After his pay raise, Matt decided to work 15 hours a week. Is Matt's supply for working elastic, inelastic, or unit-elastic?

   _____

   _____

CHAPTER 6, SECTION 1

Outlining Activity

Look through the chapter for an overview of the material. Pay attention to the main topics in the book. As you scan each section of the book, fill in the missing words in the following outline.

I. **Moving to Equilibrium**

    A. When the quantity supplied is greater than the quantity demanded, a surplus exists.

    B. When the quantity supplied is less than the quantity demanded, a _____ exists.

    C. At equilibrium, the quantity of a good that is bought and sold is the _____ quantity and the price at which the good is bought and sold is the _____ price.

    D. Price _____ when a surplus exists.

        1. With a surplus, suppliers will have inventories _____ the level they normally hold.

        2. Some sellers will _____ prices to reduce inventories; some will cut back on producing output; others will do a little of both.

        3. Price and output tend to fall until _____ is reached.

    E. Price _____ when a shortage exists.

        1. With a shortage, buyers will not be able to buy all they had hoped to buy.

        2. Some buyers will offer to pay a(n) _____ price to get sellers to sell to them instead of to other buyers.

        3. The higher prices motivate suppliers to start producing _____ output.

        4. Price and output tend to rise until _____ is reached.

II. **What Causes Equilibrium Prices to Change?**

    A. Demand increases (and supply stays the same).

        1. An increase in demand shifts the demand curve to the _____.

        2. Initially, quantity demanded is _____ than quantity supplied, so a shortage exists.

        3. Price begins to _____ until the market is in equilibrium again.

        4. Conclusion: An increase in the demand for a good will increase price, all other things remaining the same.

B. Demand decreases (and supply stays the same).

    1. A decrease in demand shifts the demand curve to the _____.

    2. Initially, quantity demanded is _____ than quantity supplied, so a surplus exists.

    3. Price begins to _____ until the market is in _____ again.

    4. Conclusion: A decrease in the demand for a good will decrease price, all other things remaining the same.

C. Supply increases (and demand stays the same).

    1. An increase in supply shifts the supply curve to the _____.

    2. Initially, quantity supplied is _____ than quantity demanded, so a surplus exists.

    3. Price begins to _____ until the market is in _____ again.

    4. Conclusion: An increase in the supply of a good will decrease price, all other things remaining the same.

D. Supply decreases (and demand stays the same).

    1. A decrease in supply shifts the supply curve to the _____.

    2. Initially, quantity supplied is _____ than quantity demanded, so a shortage exists.

    3. Price begins to _____ until the market is in equilibrium again.

    4. Conclusion: A decrease in the supply of a good will increase price, all other things remaining the same.

III. Changes in Supply and in Demand at the Same Time

A. The change in equilibrium _____ will be determined by which changes more, supply or demand.

B. If _____ increases more than _____, the equilibrium price goes up.

C. If _____ increases more than _____, the equilibrium price goes down.

IV. Does It Matter if Price Is at Its Equilibrium Level?

A. When all markets are in equilibrium, there are no _____ or

_____ of any good or service.

B. When market prices are below equilibrium prices, _____ occur. Buyers

will complain that they can't buy some goods they are willing and able to buy.

C. When market prices are above equilibrium prices, _____ occur. Sellers

complain that they can't sell some goods they are willing and able to sell.

V. Price Is a Signal

A. Price is a signal passed along by buyers to sellers.

B. When demand falls, price goes down and buyers are signaling sellers to produce

_____.

C. When demand rises, price goes up and buyers are signaling to sellers to produce

_____.

VI. What Are Price Controls?

A. A price _____ is a legislated price that is below the equilibrium price.

B. A price _____ is a legislated price that is above the equilibrium price.

VII. Price Controls and the Amount of Exchange

A. Price controls decrease the amount of exchange (trade) that occurs.

B. Price controls limit the opportunities people have to make themselves

_____.

VIII. Price and Speculators

A. Speculators do things they hope will earn them profits (such as buying and selling specific

goods).

B. Speculators reduce the variability in prices from one year to the next by reallocating supply

between years.

CHAPTER 6, SECTION 1

Just the Facts Handout

Moving to Equilibrium

Supply and demand work together to determine price. A **surplus** exists if the quantity supplied of a good is greater than the quantity demanded. When a surplus exists, the price of the good will fall. A **shortage** exists if the quantity demanded of a good is greater than the quantity supplied. When a shortage exists, the price of the good will rise.

A market is in **equilibrium** when the quantity demanded of a good equals the quantity supplied. **Equilibrium quantity** is the quantity of a good bought and sold in a market that is in equilibrium. **Equilibrium price** is the price at which a good is bought and sold in a market that is in equilibrium.

Why Does Price Fall When a Surplus Occurs?

With a surplus, suppliers will not be able to sell all they had hoped to sell. Their **inventories** (stock of goods on hand) will grow beyond normal levels. Some suppliers will lower prices to reduce their inventories. Some suppliers will cut back on producing output. Other suppliers will do a little of both. Price and output tend to fall until equilibrium is achieved. (See Exhibit 6-2 on page 146 of your textbook.)

Why Does Price Rise When There Is a Shortage?

With a shortage, buyers will not be able to buy all they had hoped to buy. Some buyers will offer to pay a higher price to get sellers to sell to them rather than to other buyers. The higher prices will motivate suppliers to start producing more output. Price and output tend to rise until equilibrium is achieved. (See Exhibit 6-2 on page 146 of your textbook.)

What Causes Equilibrium Prices to Change?

For the equilibrium price to change, either supply or demand has to change.

Demand Changes Cause Changes to Equilibrium Price

Recall from Chapter 4 that income, preferences, prices of related goods, number of buyers, and future price can shift the demand curve for a good.

An increase in demand shifts the demand curve to the right. An increase in the demand for a good will increase price, all other things remaining the same.

A decrease in demand shifts the demand curve to the left. A decrease in the demand for a good will decrease price, all other things remaining the same.

Supply Changes Cause Changes to Equilibrium Price

Recall from Chapter 5 that resource prices, technology, taxes, subsidies, quotas, number of sellers, future price, and weather can shift the supply curve for a good.

An increase in supply causes the supply curve to shift to the right. An increase in the supply of a good will decrease the price, all other things remaining the same.

A decrease in supply causes the supply curve to shift to the left. A decrease in the supply of a good will increase the price, all other things remaining the same.

Changes in Supply and in Demand at the Same Time

The change in equilibrium price will be determined by which changes more, supply or demand. If both demand and supply increase and demand increases more than supply, the equilibrium price increases. If supply increases more than demand, the equilibrium price decreases.

Does It Matter if Price Is at Its Equilibrium Level?

There are no shortages or surpluses of any good or service when all markets are in equilibrium. Neither buyers nor sellers would have any complaints. This is not the case when market prices are below or above equilibrium prices.

If market prices are below equilibrium prices, shortages occur. In shortages, buyers complain that they can't buy some goods they are willing and able to buy. If market prices are above equilibrium prices, surpluses occur. In surpluses, sellers complain that they can't sell some goods they are willing and able to sell.

Price Is a Signal

Price acts as a signal that is passed along by buyers to sellers. As price goes down, buyers are saying to sellers "produce less of this good." As price goes up, buyers are saying to sellers "produce more of this good."

What Are Price Controls?

A legislated price that is below the equilibrium price is called a **price ceiling**. A legislated price that is above the equilibrium price is called a **price floor**.

A price ceiling creates a shortage in the market. A price floor creates a surplus in the market. (See Exhibit 6-5 on page 152 of your textbook.)

Price Controls and the Amount of Exchange

Price controls (price ceilings and price floors) bring about less exchange (less trade) than would exist without them. If price controls decrease the amount of exchange that occurs, we must conclude that price controls limit the opportunities people have to make themselves better off.

Price and Speculators

Speculators do things they hope will earn them profits, such as buying and selling specific goods (such as corn). If speculators expect that there will be a shortage of corn the following year (perhaps due to an expected drought) they may purchase more corn and take it off the market with the expectation that they will be able to sell it at a higher profit the following year. Speculators do not always guess correctly, but when they do they make a profit.

Speculators reduce the variability in prices from one year to the next by reallocating supply between years. Most economists would say that they help society by preparing and adjusting for expected changes (such as a possible drought) in the marketplace.

Answer questions 1–6 in the Section 1 Assessment on page 155 of your textbook.

CHAPTER 6, SECTION 2
Outlining Activity

Look through the chapter for an overview of the material. Pay attention to the main topics in the book. As you scan each section of the book, fill in the missing words in the following outline.

I. Why the Long Lines for Concert Tickets?

    A. When people go away without being able to buy what they came to buy, it means that quantity demanded _____ quantity supplied, resulting in a shortage in the market.

    B. When a shortage exists, eventually price will _____ to its equilibrium level.

    C. The problem in the rock concert example is that the tickets were bought and sold before the seller realized a shortage of tickets would occur.

    D. If the seller had charged the equilibrium price, there would be no shortage, no long lines, and no one turned away without a ticket. (See Exhibit 6-6 on page 157 of your textbook.)

II. The Difference in Prices for Candy Bars, Bread, and Houses

    A. In general, the price of a candy bar is approximately the same in Toledo, Ohio, and Miami, Florida. This is true for many other goods also.

    B. Suppose that at a particular point in time, the price of candy bars is $2 in Toledo and $1 in Miami because the demand for candy bars is _____ in Toledo.

        1. Given the price difference, the suppliers of candy bars will prefer to sell more of their product in Toledo than in Miami. The supply of candy bars will _____ in Toledo and _____ in Miami.

        2. When the suppliers adjust their distribution levels, the price of candy bars will _____ in Toledo and _____ in Miami.

        3. Only when the price of candy bars is the same in Toledo and Miami will suppliers no longer have an incentive to rearrange the supply of candy bars in the two cities.

    C. Now consider houses in different cities—San Francisco and Louisville.

        1. Housing prices are much higher in San Francisco than in Louisville because the difference between demand and supply (_____ demand, _____ supply) is greater in San Francisco than it is in Louisville.

2. If houses were candy bars or bread, suppliers would shift their supply from Louisville to San Francisco. However, houses are built on land, and the price of the land is part of the price of a house. Suppliers cannot move land from Louisville to San Francisco.

3. When the supply of a good cannot be moved in response to a difference in price between cities, _____ for this good are likely to remain different in these cities.

III. Supply and Demand at the Movies

A. If you want to see a movie on Friday night, you may have to pay $8. The same movie at 11 a.m. on Tuesday may cost only $3.50.

B. The price difference depends on _____ and _____.

C. The supply of seats in the theater is the same Friday night as Tuesday morning.

D. The demand to see a movie on Friday night is _____ than on Tuesday morning, and the _____ demand makes for a higher price.

IV. Supply and Demand on a Freeway

A. There is a certain supply of freeway space—a certain number of lanes and miles. People also have a demand to drive on freeways.

B. The demand is _____ at 8 a.m. on Monday, when people are driving to work, than at 11 p.m.

C. For most freeways, the price of driving on the freeway is zero. Most freeways do not have tolls.

D. At 11 p.m. the demand curve for freeway space and the supply curve of freeway space intersect at zero price. There is neither a(n) _____ nor a(n) _____ of freeway space. People are using the freeway, but the traffic is moving easily without congestion.

E. At 8 a.m. with a zero price—no toll—the quantity demanded of freeway space is greater than the quantity supplied, resulting in a shortage of freeway space. The freeway is congested.

V. Supply and Demand on the Gridiron

A. Suppose a football team needs three people who can play tight end. In economic terms, the quantity supplied of tight end positions is three. Also suppose 30 people want to try out for the position of tight end. So, the quantity demanded of tight end positions is 30.

B. Because quantity demanded is _____ than quantity supplied, a shortage of tight end positions results.

C. When a shortage of anything occurs in a competitive market, the price of that thing rises.

D. The "price" of being a tight end will rise, not in dollars but in a different way. People will have to "pay" to be a tight end with hard work and skill.

E. If only five people wanted to be a tight end, the shortage of tight end positions would be _____. The "price" of being a tight end would not rise as much to bring supply and demand into equilibrium.

VI. Supply and Demand on the College Campus

    A. Different colleges require a different grade point average (GPA) or standardized test score (SAT or ACT) to be admitted. The reason for the difference is supply and demand.

    B. Suppose that both college A and college B will admit 2,000 students to its entering freshman class next year. Each college charges $15,000 a semester in tuition.

        1. The quantity supplied of open spots and the tuition are the same at each college. But at college B, 4,000 students apply for the 2,000 spots, and at college A, 12,000 students apply for the 2,000 spots. The shortage at college A is greater than the shortage at college B, so the "price" to get into college A will rise _____ than it will rise at college B.

    C. The "price" of getting into college is usually measured in terms of high school academic performance (in other words, GPA and SAT or ACT scores.)

    D. The greater the demand to get into a college compared to supply, the higher the GPA and standardized test scores required to get into that college, or the higher the "_____" a student must pay in terms of grades.

VII. Necessary Conditions for a High Income: High Demand, Low Supply

    A. Many people sell their labor services instead of goods. The "price" they receive is usually called a(n) _____.

    B. A wage is determined by supply and demand. To receive a high wage, _____ must be high and _____ low.

    C. Demand is high for both restaurant servers and computer scientists. Computer scientists earn _____ than servers because _____ is _____ for servers than it is for computer scientists.

VIII. Behavioral and Experimental Economics

    A. *Behavioral economics* studies the role that social, cognitive, and emotional factors have on economic decision making.

    B. *Experimental economics* applies _____ methods to study economic decision making.

    C. Behavioral and experimental economics show that people do not always make rational decisions.

CHAPTER 6, SECTION 2

Just the Facts Handout

Why the Long Lines for Concert Tickets?

When quantity demanded exceeds quantity supplied, the result is a shortage in the market. A market shortage causes price to rise to its equilibrium level. A shortage of tickets to a rock concert results when the ticket price is below equilibrium price. The ticket price is below equilibrium price if the tickets are bought and sold before the seller realizes that a shortage of tickets will occur at the ticket price.

The Difference in Prices for Candy Bars, Bread, and Houses

In general, no matter where you go in the United States, the price of a candy bar is about the same. This is true for many other goods, such as a loaf of bread. However, house prices are not the same everywhere in the United States. Supply and demand explain why some prices are the same everywhere and other prices are different.

Suppose the price of candy bars is $2 in Toledo and $1 in Miami because the demand for candy bars is higher in Toledo. Given the price difference, the suppliers of candy bars will prefer to sell more of their product in Toledo than in Miami. So, the supply of candy bars will increase in Toledo and decrease in Miami. The change in supply will cause the price of candy bars to decrease in Toledo and increase in Miami. When the price of candy bars is the same in Toledo and Miami, suppliers no longer have an incentive to rearrange the supply of candy bars in the two cities.

Housing prices are much higher in San Francisco than in Louisville because of more demand and less supply in San Francisco than in Louisville. If houses were candy bars, suppliers would shift their supply from Louisville to San Francisco. However, houses are built on land, and the price of the land is part of the price of a house. The supply of some goods (like land) cannot be moved in response to a difference in price between cities. Prices for these goods are likely to remain different in different cities.

Supply and Demand at the Movies

A movie on Friday night may cost $8, but the same movie at 11 a.m. on Tuesday may cost only $3.50. The demand to see a movie is higher on Friday night than it is on Tuesday morning. The higher demand makes for a higher price.

Supply and Demand on a Freeway

The supply of freeway space is a certain number of lanes and miles. People have a demand to drive on freeways. On a Monday, the demand is higher at 8 a.m., when people are driving to work, than it is at 11 p.m.

For most freeways, the price of driving on the freeway is zero. Most freeways do not have tolls. In Exhibit 6-7(a) on page 159 of your textbook, notice that the demand curve for freeway space and the supply curve of freeway space intersect at zero price at 11 p.m. There is neither a shortage nor a surplus of freeway space. Traffic moves easily without congestion. The freeway is in equilibrium.

However, at 8 a.m. with zero price, the quantity demanded of freeway space is greater than the quantity supplied. The result is a shortage of freeway space. The freeway is congested.

Supply and Demand on the Gridiron

Suppose a football team needs three people to play tight end—the quantity supplied of tight end positions is three. Also suppose 30 people want to try out for the position of tight end—the quantity demanded of tight end positions is 30. Because quantity demanded is greater than quantity supplied, a shortage of tight end positions results.

When a shortage of anything occurs in a competitive market, the price of that thing rises. The "price" of being a tight end, in terms of hard work and skill, will rise.

Supply and Demand on the College Campus

The grade point average (GPA) or standardized test score (SAT or ACT) required for college entrance is different at different colleges. One college may require a GPA of 3.0 and an SAT score of 1550, while another requires a GPA of 3.8 and an SAT score of 2100. The different requirements are due to supply and demand: The higher the demand to get into a particular college, the higher the entrance requirements at that college.

Necessary Conditions for a High Income: High Demand, Low Supply

The wage a person receives for labor services is determined by supply and demand. For someone to receive a high wage, demand must be high and supply low. For supply to be low, few people must know how to perform the job. For example, demand is high for both restaurant servers and computer scientists. Computer scientists earn higher wages than do servers because supply is higher for servers than it is for computer scientists.

Behavioral and Experimental Economics

Behavioral economics studies the role that social, cognitive, and emotional factors have on economic decision making. *Experimental economics* applies experimental methods to study economic decision making.

Experiment 1: The Ultimatum Game

This experiment suggests that people turn down lopsided offers because they view the split as unfair. This goes against the rational-actor model in economics, which assumes that people are rational and would choose an unfair benefit versus receiving no benefit.

Experiment 2: The Disease Problem

This experiment points out that people decide differently based on how a situation is framed. In economics, the term *framing* refers to how a problem is presented.

Experiment 3: Coffee Mugs

This experiment investigates a concept called the *endowment effect*—that people want to be paid much more to give up an object than they would be willing to pay for the same object. The endowment effect is often present when buying and selling a house.

Instinct and Choice

Mainstream economics is often described as a science of choice because economists study the choices of buyers, sellers, producers, borrowers, lenders, and so on. However, some have argued that if behavioral economics continues to find that people are not always rational, then economics will become more a science of instincts and less a science of choice.

Answer questions 1-4 in the Section 2 Assessment on page 165 of your textbook.

CHAPTER 6

Graphic Organizer Activity

Supply the missing words in the blank spaces of this graphic organizer.

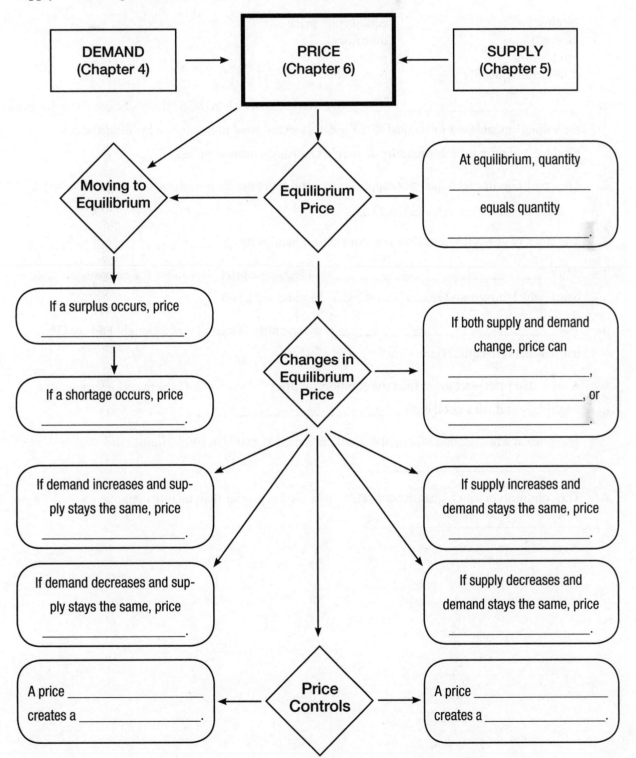

CHAPTER 6

Vocabulary Activity

For each question, fill in the blank with the correct term from the following list.

surplus   equilibrium price
shortage   inventory
equilibrium   price ceiling
equilibrium quantity   price floor

1. _____ in a market exists when the quantity of a good that buyers are willing and able to buy is equal to the quantity of the good that sellers are willing and able to produce and offer for sale (quantity demanded equals quantity supplied).

2. The condition in which quantity supplied of a good is greater than quantity demanded is called a(n) _____.

3. The stock of goods that a business or store has on hand is its _____.

4. A(n) _____ is a legislated price—set above the equilibrium price—below which buyers and sellers cannot legally buy and sell a good.

5. The _____ is the quantity of a good that is bought and sold in a market that is in equilibrium.

6. A legislated price—set lower than the equilibrium price—above which buyers and sellers cannot legally buy and sell a good is a(n) _____.

7. The price at which a good is bought and sold in a market that is in equilibrium is the _____.

8. The condition in which quantity demanded of a good is greater than quantity supplied is a(n) _____.

CHAPTER 6
Working with Graphs and Tables Activity

Use the graph to answer the questions. Write your answers on the lines provided.

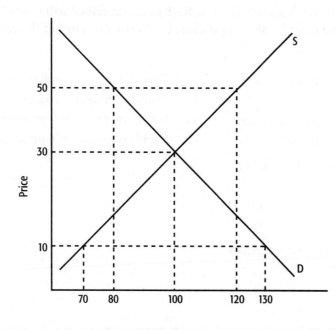

1. The equilibrium price in this market is _____.

2. The equilibrium quantity in this market is _____ units.

3. At a price of $50, the quantity supplied is _____ units and the quantity demanded is _____ units. So, a _____ of _____ units exists.

4. At a price of $10, the quantity supplied is _____ units and the quantity demanded is _____ units. So, a _____ of _____ units exists.

5. Suppose that demand increased for the good shown in the graph. At a price of $10, the _____ would _____.

CHAPTER 6

Practice Test

Matching

A business in a summer lake resort town rents jet skis. Each event described will result in a change in demand or supply and price for the rental business. Write the letter of the correct result in the blank.

1. _____ The town is hit with extremely cold and rainy weather.

2. _____ The peak summer months bring large numbers of vacationers to the town.

3. _____ More firms that rent jet skis open up businesses in the town.

4. _____ The price of renting motor boats (a substitute for jet skis) decreases.

5. _____ The price of jet ski fuel (a complement of jet skis) increases.

a. Demand increases and price rises.

b. Demand decreases and price falls.

c. Supply increases and price falls.

d. Supply decreases and price rises.

True or False

For each of these statements, place a T in the blank if the statement is true or an F if the statement is false.

1. _____ If the owner of a coffee shop charges a price for cappuccino that is below the market equilibrium price, the owner will notice that more people are willing and able to buy cappuccino than she is willing and able to sell.

2. _____ If the demand for seeing movies increases and the supply of movies is constant, we would expect the price of a movie ticket to decrease.

3. _____ If there is a shortage of 40 prom tickets and the quantity demanded is 225 tickets, the quantity supplied must equal 265 tickets.

4. _____ If the supply of a good increases by more than its demand increases, the equilibrium price will rise.

5. _____ If the demand for a good increases more than the supply of the good increases, then the price of the good will increase.

6. _____ If the price of a good is $10, the quantity demanded is 100 units, and the quantity supplied is 130 units, then the equilibrium price for the good is greater than $10.

7. _____ A shortage exists when quantity supplied is greater than quantity demanded.

8. _____ If candy bars sell for $5 each in Miami and for $2 each in Tulsa, then supplies of candy bars will move from Tulsa to Miami.

9. _____ The higher the demand for positions on a sports team relative to the supply of positions, the better chance you have to get on the team.

10. _____ The higher the demand to get into a particular college, the higher its entrance requirements.

Short Answer

Write your answers on the lines provided.

1. Yellowstone National Park charges a fee of $10 per group of campers. Each year, hundreds of campers are turned away from Yellowstone because all of the campsites are full. Use the concepts of supply and demand to explain why there is such a shortage of campsites at Yellowstone.

_____

_____

_____

_____

2. How could the Yellowstone Park officials in question 1 reduce the shortage without providing more campsites?

_____

_____

_____

3. You want to purchase tickets to see the group Coldplay. You find out that front row seats are $75 dollars while seats in the upper deck of the arena are only $30. Explain why the tickets have different prices.

_____

_____

_____

4. Why do stores cut prices on their goods after the Christmas holiday? Explain using supply and demand.

_____

_____

_____

5. According to behavioral economics, why do people turn down lopsided offers even though if they do they may end up with nothing?

_____

_____

_____

_____

CHAPTER 7, SECTION 1
Outlining Activity

Look through the chapter for an overview of the material. Pay attention to the main topics in the book. As you scan each section of the book, fill in the missing words in the following outline.

I. Why Do Business Firms Exist?

    A. Business _____ are organizations that use resources to produce goods and services that are sold to consumers, other businesses, or the government.

    B. Most businesses exist because people working together can produce more than the sum of what individuals working alone can produce.

II. Why Are Bosses Necessary?

    A. _____ is putting forth less than the agreed-to effort.

    B. Choosing someone to be the _____, or boss, can reduce shirking.

    C. The monitor can be kept from shirking by making him or her a(n) _____ claimant of the firm.

III. Three Types of Business Firms

    A. A sole _____ is a business that is owned by one individual who makes all business decisions, receives all the profits or takes all the losses of the firm, and is legally responsible for the debts of the firm.

        1. Advantages of sole proprietorships: easy to form and to dissolve; all decision-making power resides with the sole proprietor; profit is _____ only once.

        2. Disadvantages of sole proprietorships: proprietor faces _____ liability; limited ability to raise funds for business expansion; usually ends with the retirement or death of the proprietor.

    B. A(n) _____ is a business that is owned by two or more co-owners, called partners, who share profits and are legally responsible for debts.

        1. Advantages of partnerships: benefits of _____ can be realized; profit is taxed only once.

        2. Disadvantages of partnerships: partners face unlimited liability; decision making can be complex and frustrating.

C. A(n) _____ is a legal entity that can conduct business in its own name in the same way that an individual does. A corporation is owned by its stockholders—people who buy _____ of stock. A share of stock gives the purchaser a share of the ownership of the corporation.

   1. Advantages of corporations: owners (stockholders) have _____ liability; corporation continues if owners sell their shares of stock or die; usually able to raise large sums of money.

   2. Disadvantages of corporations: _____ taxation; corporations are complicated to set up.

   3. The stockholders, the owners of the corporation, elect the board of directors. The board of directors determines corporate policies and goals.

   4. A corporation can raise money by borrowing from a bank or other lending institution, selling _____, or issuing additional shares of _____.

   5. A corporation is under no legal obligation to pay stockholders. _____ purchasers have lent money to the corporation. The corporation must repay these loans, along with extra payments.

IV. The Franchise

A. A(n) _____ is a contract by which a firm (usually a corporation) lets a person or group use its name and sell its goods or services. In return, the person or group must make certain payments and meet certain requirements.

B. The corporation, or parent company, is called the _____.

C. The person or group that buys the franchise is called the _____.

D. McDonald's, Burger King, Wendy's, Pizza Hut, Domino's Pizza, and Taco Bell are all franchises.

V. What Ethical and Social Responsibilities Do Businesses Have?

A. Ralph Nader, the consumer advocate, believes that businesses have ethical and social responsibilities.

   1. Businesses should treat both _____ and _____ well.

   2. Businesses _____ donate funds to meet social needs in the community.

B. Milton Friedman, the winner of the 1976 Nobel Prize in economics, believes that businesses should meet certain ethical standards.

    1. Businesses should engage in free and open _____.

    2. Businesses should not lie to the public.

    3. Businesses _____ donate to charities.

C. _____ information exists when one party has information that another party to a transaction does not have.

VI. Where Will Firms Locate?

A. The competition for _____ drives similar firms to locate near each other.

B. For example, gas stations are often located near each other. In many towns, car dealerships are located in the same vicinity. Many of the major financial firms are headquartered in New York City.

CHAPTER 7, SECTION 1

Just the Facts Handout

Why Do Business Firms Exist?

Business firms are organizations that use resources to produce goods and services that are sold to consumers, other firms, or the government. Business firms exist because people working together can be more effective than people working individually.

Why Are Bosses Necessary?

After a firm is formed, people in the firm will shirk. **Shirking** is working less hard than one agreed to work. To deal with this problem, firms choose a monitor (the boss), and give him or her the ability to hire and fire employees. One way that firms make sure the monitor doesn't shirk is to make him or her the residual claimant. A residual claimant receives the excess of revenues over costs (profits) as income.

Three Types of Firms

Sole Proprietorship

A **sole proprietorship** is a business that is owned by one individual who makes all the business decisions, receives all the profits or takes all the losses of the firm, and is legally responsible for the debts of the firm.

Three advantages of sole proprietorships are as follows:
1. Sole proprietorships are easy to form and to dissolve.
2. All decision-making power resides with the sole proprietor.
3. The profit of the firm is taxed only once, as personal income taxes (taxes paid on your income).

Three disadvantages of sole proprietorships are as follows:
1. Sole proprietors face unlimited liability, which means that their personal assets may be used to pay off the debts of the firm.
2. Sole proprietors do not find it easy to borrow funds because lenders are not eager to lend funds to business firms whose success depends on one person.
3. Sole proprietorships usually end with the retirement or death of the proprietor.

Partnership

A **partnership** is a business that is owned by two or more co-owners, called partners, who share profits the business earns and who are legally responsible for debts incurred by the firm.

Two advantages of partnerships are as follows:
1. Benefits of specialization can be realized.
2. The profit of the partnership is taxed only once. The partners pay only personal income taxes.

Two disadvantages of partnerships are as follows:
1. General partners face unlimited liability. The liability of a limited partner is restricted to the amount she or he has invested in the firm.
2. Decision making in a partnership can be complicated and frustrating.

Corporation

A **corporation** is a legal entity that can conduct business in its own name in the same way that an individual does. A corporation is owned by its stockholders. **Stockholders** are people who buy shares of stock in a corporation. A share of stock represents a claim on the assets of the corporation. **Assets** are anything of value to which the firm has legal claim.

Three advantages of corporations are as follows:

1. The owners (the stockholders) have **limited liability**. They are not personally responsible for the debts of the corporation.

2. Corporations continue to exist even if one or more owners sell their shares or die.

3. Corporations are usually able to raise large sums of money by selling stock.

Two disadvantages of corporations are as follows:

1. Corporations are subject to double taxation: Their profits are subject to the corporate income tax. Their dividends (shares of the profits distributed to stockholders) are subject to personal income taxes.

2. Corporations are complicated to set up.

As a group, the stockholders are the most important persons in a corporation. They are its owners, and they elect the members of the board of directors. The **board of directors** determines corporate policies and goals.

Corporations can raise money by borrowing from banks and other lending institutions. They can also sell bonds, and they can sell additional shares of stock. These actions are sometimes referred to as issuing debt and issuing stock.

A bond is a statement of debt issued by a corporation—an IOU, or a piece of paper on which is written a promise to pay. This promise has two parts: (1) The corporation promises to pay the face value (or par value) of the bond on a particular date (called the maturity date). (2) The corporation also promises to pay the coupon rate multiplied by the face value of the bond each year until the maturity date.

The key difference between bondholders and stockholders is that the corporation is under no legal obligation to pay stockholders. Bond purchasers have lent money to the corporation, so the corporation must repay these loans, along with extra payments.

The Franchise

A **franchise** is a contract by which a firm lets a person or group use its name and sell its goods or services. In return, the person or group must make certain payments and meet certain requirements. The corporation, or parent company, is called the **franchiser**. The person or group that buys the franchise is called the **franchisee**.

What Ethical and Social Responsibilities Do Businesses Have?

Ralph Nader, the consumer advocate, believes that businesses have ethical and social responsibilities. They should treat both customers and employees well and should donate funds to meet social needs in the community.

According to Milton Friedman, the winner of the 1976 Nobel Prize in economics, businesses have the ethical responsibilities of engaging in free and open competition and not lying to the public. However, businesses should forget about giving money to charities.

Asymmetric information exists in a transaction when one party has information that another party does not have. Most people today believe that businesses have the ethical responsibility to tell their customers everything that might be considered important to buying a product. In addition, people generally feel that businesses should tell possible employees everything that is significant about jobs they are trying to fill.

Where Will Firms Locate?

Similar firms have an incentive to locate near each other. The competition for customers drives them to this position.

Answer questions 1–5 in the Section 1 Assessment on page 189 of your textbook.

CHAPTER 7, SECTION 2

Outlining Activity

Look through the chapter for an overview of the material. Pay attention to the main topics in the book. As you scan each section of the book, fill in the missing words in the following outline.

I. Fixed and Variable Costs

A. _____ costs, or expenses, are the same no matter how many units of a

good are _____.

B. Variable costs, or expenses, _____ with the number of units of a good

produced.

C. Total costs are the sum of fixed costs and variable costs.

> Total costs = Fixed costs + Variable costs

II. Average Total Cost

A. _____ total cost (ATC), or per-unit cost, is total cost (TC) divided by

quantity of output (Q).

> Average total cost (ATC) $= \dfrac{TC}{Q}$

III. Marginal Cost: An Important Cost Concept

A. Marginal cost is the _____ in total cost that results from producing a(n)

_____ unit of output. In other words, marginal cost is the additional cost

of producing an additional unit of a good.

B. Marginal cost (MC) is the change in total cost (ΔTC) divided by the change in quantity of

output (ΔQ). (In economics, the triangle symbol, Δ, means "change in.")

> Marginal cost (MC) $= \dfrac{\Delta TC}{\Delta Q}$

CHAPTER 7, SECTION 2

Just the Facts Handout

Fixed and Variable Costs

A cost, or expense, that is the same no matter how many units of a good are produced is a **fixed cost**. For example, Olivia pays $1,500 in insurance for her small store each year, no matter how much she sells. The $1,500 insurance payment is a fixed cost.

A cost, or expense, that changes with the number of units of a good produced is a **variable cost**. For example, an increase in labor cost goes along with an increase in the number of goods produced. This cost for labor is a variable cost.

Total cost is the sum of fixed costs and variable costs. For example, if fixed costs are $2,000 for the month and variable costs are $750, then total cost is $2,750 for the month.

Average Total Cost

Average total cost (ATC), or per-unit cost, is total cost (TC) divided by quantity of output (Q). For example, if total cost is $6,000 and 1,000 units of a good are produced, then average total cost is $6 per unit ($6,000 ÷ 1,000 = $6).

Marginal Cost: An Important Cost Concept

The change in total cost that results from producing an additional unit of output is called **marginal cost**. Marginal cost equals the change in total cost divided by the change in quantity of output.

For example, suppose Harry has produced 10 chairs at a total cost of $1,000. When Harry produces one more chair (the 11th chair), his total cost rises to $1,088. The marginal cost of chairs is $88—the additional cost of producing the 11th chair.

Answer questions 1–3 in the Section 2 Assessment on page 193 of your textbook.

CHAPTER 7, SECTION 3

Outlining Activity

Look through the chapter for an overview of the material. Pay attention to the main topics in the book. As you scan each section of the book, fill in the missing words in the following outline.

I. Total Revenue and Marginal Revenue

A. Total revenue is the _____ of a good times the _____ sold.

B. Marginal revenue is the _____ revenue from selling an _____ unit of a good. Marginal revenue equals the change in total revenue divided by the change in the quantity of output sold.

$$\text{Marginal revenue (MR)} = \frac{\Delta TR}{\Delta Q}$$

II. Firms Have to Answer Questions

A. One question is, How much should we produce?

B. A second question is, What price should we charge?

III. How Much Will a Firm Produce?

A. Firms compare _____ with _____ to decide how much to produce.

B. A firm should produce additional units of its good until marginal revenue is _____ marginal cost.

IV. What Every Firm Wants: To Maximize Profit

A. Whenever a firm produces and sells an additional unit of a good and marginal revenue is _____ than marginal cost, the firm is adding more to its total revenue than to its total cost.

B. A firm maximizes _____ by producing the quantity of output at which MR = MC.

V. How to Compute Profit and Loss

A. To compute _____ or _____, determine total

_____ and total _____ and then find the difference.

1. To compute total cost (TC), add fixed cost (FC) to variable cost (VC).

2. To compute total revenue (TR), multiply the price of the good (P) times the quantity of units (Q) of the good sold.

3. To compute profit (or loss), subtract total _____

(_____) from total _____

(_____).

VI. How Many Workers Should the Firm Hire?

A. The law of _____ states that if we add additional units of a resource (such as labor) to another resource (such as capital) that is in fixed supply, eventually the additional output produced (as a result of hiring an additional worker) will decrease.

B. If the additional output produced by an additional worker multiplied by the price of the good is _____ than the wage paid, then the worker should be hired.

C. If the additional output produced by an additional worker multiplied by the price of the good is _____ than the wage paid, then the worker should not be hired.

CHAPTER 7, SECTION 3

Just the Facts Handout

Total Revenue and Marginal Revenue

Total revenue is the price of a good multiplied by the quantity sold. For example, if the price of a book is $15 and 100 are sold, then total revenue is $1,500.

The change in total revenue (TR) that results from selling an additional unit of output is **marginal revenue** (MR). In other words, marginal revenue is the additional revenue from selling an additional unit of a good.

For example, Harris sells toys for a price of $10 each. Harris currently sells 1,000 toys. This means that Harris's total revenue is $10,000. If Harris sells one more toy for $10, total revenue changes from $10,000 to $10,010. So, $10 is the marginal revenue.

Marginal revenue equals the change in total revenue divided by the change in the quantity of output sold.

Firms Have to Answer Questions

Firms must answer the following questions:
- How much should we produce?
- What price should we charge?

How Much Will a Firm Produce?

Firms produce as long as marginal revenue (the additional revenue of producing another unit) is greater than marginal cost (the additional cost of producing the additional unit). Look at it this way:

$$MR > MC \rightarrow \text{Produce}$$
$$MC > MR \rightarrow \text{Do not produce}$$

A firm should produce even if marginal revenue is only one penny more than marginal cost. This will bring in additional profit. Economists essentially say that it is beneficial to produce as long as marginal revenue is greater than marginal cost, even if the difference between the two is extremely small.

A business firm should continue to produce additional units of its good until marginal revenue (MR) is equal to marginal cost (MC).

What Every Firm Wants: To Maximize Profit

Profit is the difference between total revenue and total cost. A firm wants profit to be as large as possible. In other words, a firm wants to maximize profit.

Whenever a firm produces and sells an additional unit of a good and marginal revenue is greater than marginal cost, the firm is adding more to its total revenue than to its total cost. Therefore, it is maximizing profit. A firm maximizes profit by producing the quantity of output at which marginal revenue equals marginal cost.

How to Compute Profit and Loss

To compute profit or loss, a firm determines total cost and total revenue and then finds the difference between the two. Total cost is the sum of fixed costs and variable costs. Total revenue is the price of the good multiplied by the quantity of units of the good sold.

How Many Workers Should the Firm Hire?

The **law of diminishing marginal returns** states that if additional units of one resource are added to another resource in fixed supply, eventually the additional output will decrease. So, if additional workers are added to capital, eventually the additional output produced as a result of hiring an additional worker will decrease.

One way to figure out whether or not to hire an additional worker is to calculate how much "comes in" the door with the additional worker compared with how much "goes out" the door with the additional worker. What "comes in" the door is the value of the output produced by the worker. What "goes out" the door is the wage paid to the worker. As long as the additional output produced by the additional worker multiplied by the price of the good is greater than the wage paid, the worker should be hired.

Answer questions 1–3 in the Section 3 Assessment on page 203 of your textbook.

CHAPTER 7

Graphic Organizer Activity

Supply the missing words in the blank spaces of this graphic organizer.

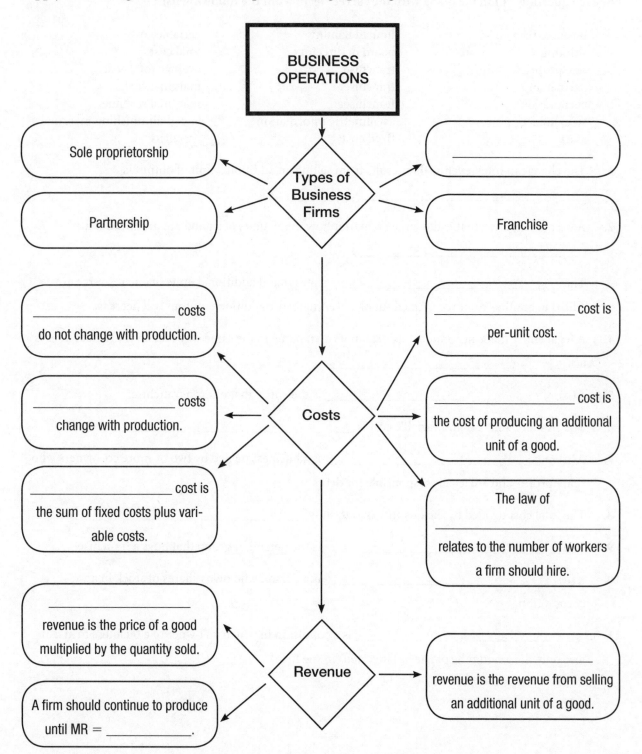

BUSINESS OPERATIONS

Types of Business Firms
- Sole proprietorship
- Partnership
- _____
- Franchise

Costs
- _____ costs do not change with production.
- _____ costs change with production.
- _____ cost is the sum of fixed costs plus variable costs.
- _____ cost is per-unit cost.
- _____ cost is the cost of producing an additional unit of a good.
- The law of _____ relates to the number of workers a firm should hire.

Revenue
- _____ revenue is the price of a good multiplied by the quantity sold.
- A firm should continue to produce until MR = _____.
- _____ revenue is the revenue from selling an additional unit of a good.

CHAPTER 7

Vocabulary Activity

For each question, fill in the blank with the correct term from the following list.

business firm	limited liability	variable cost
shirking	board of directors	total cost
sole proprietorship	franchise	average total cost
partnership	franchiser	marginal cost
corporation	franchisee	marginal revenue
stockholder	asymmetric information	law of diminishing marginal
asset	fixed cost	returns

1. The change in total revenue that results from selling an additional unit of output is

    _____.

2. A cost, or expense, that is the same no matter how many units of a good are produced is a(n)

    _____.

3. The _____ states that if additional units of one resource are

    added to another resource in fixed supply, eventually the additional output will decrease.

4. A legal entity that can conduct business in its own name in the same way that an individual does is

    a(n) _____.

5. A(n) _____ is the entity that offers a franchise.

6. The sum of fixed cost and variable cost is _____.

7. A(n) _____ is a business owned by two or more co-owners who

    share profits and are legally responsible for debts.

8. The total cost divided by the quantity of output is _____.

9. A(n) _____ is the person or group that buys a franchise.

10. A(n) _____ is a person who owns shares of stock in a

    corporation.

11. _____ is a condition in which an owner of a business firm can

    lose only the amount he or she has invested (in the firm).

12. A business that is owned by one individual who makes all business decisions, receives all the profits or incurs all the losses of the firm, and is legally responsible for the debts of the firm is a(n)

_____.

13. Anything of value to which the firm has a legal claim is a(n) _____.

14. A(n) _____ is a contract by which a firm (usually a corporation) lets a person or group use its name and sell its goods in exchange for certain payments and requirements.

15. A(n) _____ is an organization that uses resources to produce goods and services that are sold to consumers, other firms, or the government.

16. A cost, or expense, that changes with the number of units of a good produced is a(n)

_____.

17. _____ is the behavior of a worker who is putting forth less than the agreed-to effort.

18. The change in total cost that results from producing an additional unit of output is

_____.

19. The _____ is an important decision-making body in a corporation that determines corporate policies and goals.

20. _____ exists when one party to a transaction has information that another party does not.

CHAPTER 7
Working with Graphs and Tables Activity

You are considering opening an ice cream shop in Fredericksburg, Texas, a picturesque town that attracts many tourists and vacationers. Before you open your new business, you must decide which type of firm you would like to start—a sole proprietorship, a partnership, or a corporation. List the advantages and disadvantages of each of these three types of businesses in the following table.

Sole Proprietorship	
Advantages	Disadvantages

Partnership	
Advantages	Disadvantages

Corporation	
Advantages	Disadvantages

Which type of firm would you choose? Explain your answer. Write your answer on the lines provided.

_____

_____

_____

_____

_____

_____

CHAPTER 7

Practice Test

Multiple Choice

Circle the letter of the correct answer.

1. The legal responsibility of a sole proprietor or partners to pay any money owed by the business is which of the following?

   a. limited liability
   b. unlimited liability
   c. residual claimant
   d. marginal returns

2. If additional units of a resource are added to another resource in fixed supply, eventually the additional output will decrease. Which of the following does this statement describe?

   a. a franchise
   b. limited liability
   c. the law of diminishing marginal returns
   d. variable costs

3. What does total cost equal?

   a. marginal cost plus fixed cost
   b. average cost plus marginal cost
   c. average cost plus fixed cost
   d. fixed cost plus variable cost

4. What is the additional cost of producing an additional unit of a good called?

   a. marginal cost
   b. variable cost
   c. total cost
   d. fixed cost

5. What does profit (or loss) equal?

   a. marginal revenue minus marginal cost
   b. total revenue minus total cost
   c. total revenue minus fixed cost
   d. total cost minus marginal cost

6. For the month, a firm's fixed costs were $100 and its variable costs were $75. The price of the firm's good is $5, and the firm sold 50 units of its good for the month. What is the firm's profit or loss for the month?

   a. $75 profit
   b. $175 profit
   c. $50 loss
   d. cannot determine from this information

7. What type of liability do owners of corporations have?

   a. limited liability
   b. unlimited liability
   c. partial liability
   d. marginal liability

8. A corporation can raise money to finance its operations by which of the following?

   a. selling bonds
   b. borrowing from banks
   c. issuing additional shares of stock
   d. all of the above

9. A firm should produce additional units until which of the following occurs?

   a. $MR > MC$
   b. $TC = TR$
   c. $MR = \Delta TR$
   d. $MR = MC$

10. Why are bosses necessary?

    a. because employees shirk
    b. because monitors are residual claimants
    c. because monitors shirk
    d. because owners are stockholders

Short Answer

Write your answers on the lines provided.

1. One of the disadvantages of a corporation is that it is subject to double taxation. Explain what double taxation means.

   _____

   _____

   _____

2. What is the difference between using bonds or stocks to finance corporate activity?

   _____

   _____

   _____

3. What are the ethical and social responsibilities of businesses?

   _____

   _____

   _____

   _____

   _____

Guided Reading and Study Guide

CHAPTER 8, SECTION 1
Outlining Activity

Look through the chapter for an overview of the material. Pay attention to the main topics in the book. As you scan each section of the book, fill in the missing words in the following outline.

I. Four Types of Markets

   A. Market structures are defined by their characteristics, such as the number of sellers in the market, the product that sellers produce, and how easy or difficult it is to enter the market.

   B. Four types of markets are _____ competitive, _____, monopolistic _____, and _____.

II. Characteristics of a Perfectly Competitive Market

   A. The market has _____ buyers and _____ sellers.

   B. All firms sell _____ goods.

   C. Buyers and sellers have all relevant _____ about prices, product quality, sources of supply, and so on.

   D. Firms have easy _____ into and _____ out of the market.

III. Sellers in a Perfectly Competitive Market Are _____

   A. A price taker is a seller that can sell _____ its output at the equilibrium price, but can sell _____ of its output at any other price.

IV. Can Price Takers Sell for Less than the Equilibrium Price?

   A. Price takers will not sell for _____ than equilibrium price.

   B. Price takers have no reason to sell their product at _____ than equilibrium price because they can sell all their product at the higher equilibrium price.

V. Must a Perfectly Competitive Market Possess All Four Characteristics?

   A. If a seller is a price taker, then it is operating in a(n) _____ market even if all four conditions of perfect competition are not met.

VI. What Does a Perfectly Competitive Firm Do?

A. It produces the quantity of output at which marginal _____ equals marginal _____.

B. It must sell its product at the _____ because it is a price taker.

VII. Profit Is a Signal in a Perfectly Competitive Market

A. Profit acts as a(n) _____ to firms not in the market to enter the market.

B. As new firms enter the market, they _____ the supply of the good that is earning profit, and thus _____ its price.

C. As price falls, the firms' profits _____.

D. The process ends when there is no longer an incentive for firms to enter the market to obtain profit.

VIII. Profits May Be Taxed Away

A. If the profits of firms are taxed away, no new firms will enter the market.

B. _____ will not increase, and the _____ of the good will not fall.

C. The unintended effect is that consumers pay a(n) _____ price than they would have paid without the tax.

CHAPTER 8, SECTION 1

Just the Facts Handout

Four Types of Markets

Market structures are defined by their characteristics. Those characteristics include the number of sellers in the market, the product that sellers produce and sell, and how easy or difficult it is for new firms to enter the market. There are four types of market structures:

- perfectly competitive
- monopolistic
- monopolistic competitive
- oligopolistic

Characteristics of a Perfectly Competitive Market

Four characteristics of a **perfectly competitive market** are as follows:
1. The market has many buyers and many sellers.
2. All firms sell identical goods.
3. Buyers and sellers know what they need to know about prices, product quality, sources of supply, and so on.
4. Firms can enter the market easily and leave it easily.

Sellers in a Perfectly Competitive Market Are Price Takers

A seller in a perfectly competitive market will be a price taker. A **price taker** is a seller that can sell his or her goods only at the equilibrium price.

Can Price Takers Sell for Less than the Equilibrium Price?

If sellers in a perfectly competitive market want to sell their goods, they have to sell at the equilibrium price. They cannot sell their products for even one penny more. They have no reason to sell their products for less. After all, they can sell *all* their products at the equilibrium price.

So, two points are true for every price taker:
1. A price taker *cannot* sell for a price higher than the equilibrium price.
2. A price taker *will not* sell for a price lower than the equilibrium price.

Must a Perfectly Competitive Market Possess All Four Characteristics?

A market does not need to have all four characteristics to be perfectly competitive. If a seller is a price taker, then, for all practical purposes, this seller is operating in a perfectly competitive market.

What Does a Perfectly Competitive Firm Do?

A perfectly competitive firm produces the quantity of output at which marginal revenue (MR) equals marginal cost (MC). The firm sells its product for the equilibrium price determined in the market. If the equilibrium price is $10, then the firm charges $10, not $10.01 or $9.99.

Profit Is a Signal in a Perfectly Competitive Market

Being able to enter the market easily is a characteristic of a perfectly competitive market. In other words, firms that are currently not in market X can easily get into that market. As long as sellers are earning profits in market X, new firms will enter the market.

As new firms enter market X, the number of firms in the market increases. With more firms, the supply of good X increases. When the supply of a good rises, equilibrium price falls. As price falls, so does profit. Profit is total revenue minus total cost. In this case, as price falls, so do total revenue and profit.

Firms continue to enter the market until profit falls to zero and total revenue exactly equals total cost. At this point, firms will no longer gain financially if they enter market X. Once this happens, the process ends.

Profits May Be Taxed Away

Suppose the government decides to tax 100 percent of the profits of firms in a perfectly competitive market. If these firms have to pay all their profits to the government in taxes, no new firms will enter the market. Supply will not increase, and the price of the good will not fall. As a result, consumers will have to pay a higher price than they would have paid without the tax.

Answer questions 1–3 in the Section 1 Assessment on page 214 of your textbook.

CHAPTER 8, SECTION 2
Outlining Activity

Look through the chapter for an overview of the material. Pay attention to the main topics in the book. As you scan each section of the book, fill in the missing words in the following outline.

I. Characteristics of a Monopoly

    A. The monopolistic market consists of _____.

    B. The single seller sells a product that has no close _____.

    C. The _____ are high, which means that entry into the market is extremely difficult.

II. How Monopolists Differ from Perfect Competitors

    A. A monopoly firm is a price _____, or a firm that can sell some of its output at various prices.

    B. A price _____ has to "take" the equilibrium price and sell its product at this price, but a price _____ can choose from various prices.

    C. The monopoly firm, like any firm, will produce that quantity of output at which marginal _____ equals marginal _____.

    D. The monopoly firm then charges the _____ price at which it can sell its entire output.

    E. The monopoly firm must _____ for the best price through trial and error.

III. How Selling Corn or Stock Differs from Selling Cable TV Service

    A. It is rather easy for firms to determine their _____ in perfectly competitive markets.

    B. Price determination is not so easy in _____ markets.

IV. Is the Sky the Limit for the Monopolist?

    A. The monopolist is limited in the price it charges by the height of the _____ curve it faces.

V. A Monopoly Seller Is Not Guaranteed Profits

A. The monopolist sells its product for the highest possible price, but it is not guaranteed that this price will be greater than average total cost.

B. If price is not greater than average total cost, then the monopolist will not make a(n) _____.

VI. Barriers to _____

A. _____ barriers include public franchises, patents, and copyrights.

B. In some industries, firms have extremely low _____ total cost (low per-unit cost). A company that ends up the only seller of a good because of its low average total cost is called a(n) _____.

C. A firm that has exclusive _____ of a scarce resource is considered a monopoly firm.

D. A government monopoly is a monopoly that is legally _____ from competition.

E. A market monopoly is a monopoly that is not legally protected from competition.

VII. Antitrust and Monopoly

A. Antitrust laws are meant to control _____ power and to preserve and promote _____.

B. The _____, passed in 1890, states that either attempting to become a monopolist or trying to restrain trade is illegal.

C. The _____ of 1914 made certain business practices illegal when their effects "may be to substantially lessen _____ or tend to create a _____." The act prohibited two practices.

    1. Price _____, which occurs when a seller charges different buyers different prices for the same product, and when the price differences are not related to _____ differences.

    2. _____ contracts, which are arrangements whereby the sale of one product depends on the purchase of another product or products.

D. The _____, passed in 1914, declared illegal "unfair methods of competition in commerce." In particular, the act was designed to prohibit aggressive _____ acts.

E. The Robinson-Patman Act, passed in 1936, protects _____ from the competition of large and growing _____ stores.

F. The Wheeler-Lea Act, passed in 1938, empowered the _____ (FTC) to deal with false and deceptive acts or practices by businesses.

G. The government regulates _____ through price regulation and profit regulation.

   1. _____ regulation is when the government sets the price the natural monopoly can charge.

   2. _____ regulation is when the government specifies that a natural monopoly can earn only a certain rate of profit.

VIII. Are Antitrust Laws Always Applied Properly?

A. Sometimes government, through its enforcement of the antitrust laws, promotes and protects competition, and sometimes it doesn't.

CHAPTER 8, SECTION 2

Just the Facts Handout

Characteristics of a Monopoly

The three characteristics of a **monopolistic market** are as follows:
1. The market consists of one seller.
2. The single seller sells a product that has no close substitutes.
3. The **barriers to entry** are high. This means that it is very difficult to enter the market.

How Monopolists Differ from Perfect Competitors

Perfectly competitive firms are price takers. A monopoly firm (or monopolist) is a **price searcher**. A price taker has to "take" the equilibrium price and sell its product at that price. In contrast, a price searcher can choose from a list of prices. The price searcher "searches" for the price that will give it the greatest profit or the least loss. The monopolist must search for the highest price through trial and error.

The monopoly firm, like any firm, produces the quantity of output at which marginal revenue equals marginal cost.

How Selling Corn or Stock Differs from Selling Cable TV Service

A perfectly competitive firm can easily determine the selling price. For example, a corn farmer simply checks the news to find out the selling price of corn. For a monopolist, determining price is not so easy. For example, the owner of a cable TV company will not find a convenient report of prices anywhere.

Is the Sky the Limit for the Monopolist?

At some high prices, no one will be willing to buy a monopolist's good. The "height" of the demand curve limits the price a monopolist can charge. (See Exhibit 8-1 on page 217 of your textbook.)

A Monopoly Seller Is Not Guaranteed Profits

Nothing guarantees that the monopolist's price will be greater than the monopolist's average total cost. What happens if average total cost is higher than the highest price the monopolist can charge? The monopolist will not earn a profit. In this situation, the monopolist will go out of business.

Barriers to Entry

One of the three characteristics of a monopolistic market is high barriers to entry. These barriers include legal barriers, a monopolist's extremely low average total costs, and a monopolist's exclusive ownership of a scarce resource.

Legal Barriers

Legal barriers to entry in a monopoly market include public franchises, patents, and copyrights. A **public franchise** is a right that a government gives to a firm. This right allows the firm to provide a particular good or service and keeps all others from doing so. For example, the government has given the U.S. Postal Service a public franchise to deliver first-class mail.

Extremely Low Average Total Costs (Low Per-Unit Costs)

In some industries, a company may have a very low average total cost. In fact, the average total cost may be so low that the company can sell its product at a very low price and still earn a profit. When this happens, competitors may be forced out of business. Such a firm is called a **natural monopoly**.

Exclusive Ownership of a Scarce Resource

If one firm owns all the important resources to produce a product, it is considered a monopoly firm.

Government Monopoly and Market Monopoly

Some economists divide the barriers that keep firms from entering markets into two categories. One category consists of barriers that exist because the law does not allow competition. Such barriers include public franchises, patents, and copyrights. This category may be called government monopolies.

   The other category consists of barriers that exist for other reasons. These barriers include a firm's low average total cost or exclusive ownership of a resource. This category is referred to as market monopolies.

Antitrust and Monopoly

Antitrust laws are meant to control the power of monopolies. They are also intended to preserve and promote competition. Several such laws have been passed in the United States:

- *The Sherman Antitrust Act of 1890.* This law states that (1) attempting to become a monopolist is illegal and (2) trying to restrain trade is illegal.
- *The Clayton Act of 1914.* This law made it illegal for businesses to do things that would decrease competition or create a monopoly. The act made it illegal to practice price discrimination. Price discrimination occurs when a seller charges different buyers different prices for the same product and when the price differences are not related to cost differences. The act also made tying contracts illegal. A tying contract states that to purchase a particular product, the buyer must also purchase some other product or products.
- *The Federal Trade Commission Act of 1914.* This act made it illegal to drastically lower prices.
- *The Robinson-Patman Act of 1936.* The act allowed suppliers to offer special discounts to large chains only if they offered the same discounts to everyone else. Many economists believe that the Robinson-Patman Act limited competition.
- *The Wheeler-Lea Act of 1938.* This act gave the Federal Trade Commission (FTC) the power to deal with false and deceptive acts or practices by businesses. The FTC has used this power in cases involving advertising.

   The government does not usually apply antitrust laws to a natural monopoly. Instead, it often uses regulations to control the natural monopolist. For example, the government does not allow a natural monopoly to charge any price it wants. Rather, the government often sets the price that the natural monopoly can charge. Or, sometimes the government sets the rate of profit the natural monopoly can earn.

Are Antitrust Laws Always Applied Properly?

The record of government in the area of antitrust laws is mixed. Sometimes government enforces the antitrust laws in order to promote and protect competition. Sometimes it does not.

Answer questions 1–4 in the Section 2 Assessment on page 225 of your textbook.

CHAPTER 8, SECTION 3

Outlining Activity

Look through the chapter for an overview of the material. Pay attention to the main topics in the book. As you scan each section of the book, fill in the missing words in the following outline.

I. Characteristics of a Monopolistic Competitive Market

A. The monopolistic competitive market includes many buyers and many sellers.

B. Firms produce and sell _____ products.

C. Firms have _____ entry into and exit out of the market.

II. Monopolistic Competitive Firms Are Price _____

A. Monopolistic competitive firms are price searchers because they sell slightly different products.

B. They can sell at least some of their product at various prices.

III. What Do Monopolistic Competitive Firms Do?

A. Monopolistic competitive firms produce the quantity of output at which marginal _____ equals marginal _____.

B. Monopolistic competitive firms search for the _____ price per unit at which they can sell their entire output.

IV. How Are Monopolistic Competitors' Products Different?

A. Monopolistic competitors' products can be different in any way that is perceived as different by _____.

B. How the product is packaged, where it is purchased, from whom it is purchased, and whether it is delivered may make a difference to consumers.

V. Many Monopolistic Competitors Would Rather Be Monopolists

A. A monopolistic competitor may, through _____, persuade buyers that its product is much different from competitors' products. The firm then stands a better chance of becoming a monopolist.

VI. What Matters Is How Much Competition a Seller Faces

A. The degree of competition that a seller faces depends on two factors.

1. How close to _____ a seller's product is.

2. How _____ it is for new sellers to enter the market.

CHAPTER 8, SECTION 3

Just the Facts Handout

Characteristics of a Monopolistic Competitive Market

The three characteristics of a **monopolistic competitive market** are as follows:
1. The market includes many buyers and many sellers.
2. Firms produce and sell slightly different products.
3. Firms can easily enter and leave the market.

Monopolistic Competitive Firms Are Price Searchers

Firms in a monopolistic competitive market are price searchers because they sell slightly different products. Consumers cannot find identical goods produced by different sellers. Each good is slightly different from all other goods.

What Do Monopolistic Competitive Firms Do?

Like perfectly competitive firms and monopoly firms, monopolistic competitive firms have to answer two questions:
1. How much do we produce?
2. What price do we charge?
They produce the quantity of output at which marginal revenue equals marginal cost. They answer the second question the same way monopoly sellers answer it. They search for the highest price at which they can sell everything they produce.

How Are Monopolistic Competitors' Products Different?

Monopolistic competitors' products can be different in any way that consumers see as different. For example, suppose location makes a difference to consumers. Then two physically identical products sold at different locations are slightly different products.

In short, the physical properties of a product may not be all that matters to consumers. Consumers may care about how the product is packaged, where it is purchased, from whom it is purchased, and whether it is delivered.

Many Monopolistic Competitors Would Rather Be Monopolists

A monopolistic competitor may use advertising to tell consumers that its product is different from its competitors' products. If consumers believe that the product is different enough, the firm might become a monopolist for that product.

What Matters Is How Much Competition a Seller Faces

Sellers in different types of markets face different amounts of competition. How much competition a seller faces—much, some, very little, none—mostly depends on two factors. One factor is how close to unique a seller's product is. The second factor is how easy it is for new sellers to enter the market.

Answer questions 1–4 in the Section 3 Assessment on page 232 of your textbook.

CHAPTER 8, SECTION 4

Outlining Activity

Look through the chapter for an overview of the material. Pay attention to the main topics in the book. As you scan each section of the book, fill in the missing words in the following outline.

I. Characteristics of an Oligopolistic Market

A. The oligopolistic market has _____ sellers.

B. Firms produce and sell either _____ or _____ products.

C. The barriers to entry are _____, which means that entry into the market is difficult.

II. Oligopolistic Firms Are Price _____

III. How Much Competition Do Oligopolists Face?

A. An oligopolist faces fairly stiff competition from _____ sellers.

B. An oligopolist does not face too much _____ from new sellers.

IV. Identifying Oligopolistic Industries

A. Economists determine whether a market is oligopolistic by the _____ of sales accounted for by the top four firms in the industry.

B. If only a(n) _____ firms account for a large _____ of sales, then the market is considered oligopolistic.

V. Oligopoly and _____: Looking over Your Shoulder

A. An oligopoly is more likely to base its behavior on what other sellers do than if it is one of many sellers.

VI. Cartels

A. A(n) _____ agreement among firms specifies that they will act in a coordinated way to _____ the competition among them and raise their _____.

B. In the United States, cartel agreements are _____.

C. Firms that enter into cartel agreements usually break them.

VII. Price Discrimination

A. Price discrimination exists when a seller charges different _____ to different buyers and the price differences do not reflect cost differences.

B. Certain conditions must be present before a seller can price discriminate.

    1. Different customers must be willing and able to pay _____ prices for a good.

    2. The seller requires a way to tell who is willing to pay different prices. For example, a seller needs to know who is willing to pay $10 and who is willing to pay only $8.

    3. It has to be impossible, or extremely costly, for the good that is purchased by one customer to be _____ to another.

C. Price discrimination is illegal in the United States under certain conditions.

    1. It is illegal if a seller price discriminates, and, as a result, injures _____ .

    2. It is usually illegal if one of the discriminating sales crosses _____ lines. For example, a seller sells a good for less in one state than in another state and the difference in price is not warranted by a difference in costs.

D. Price discrimination is not usually considered illegal if no injury occurs to competition or if the seller can show that charging a lower price to some customers is necessary to adequately compete in the market.

CHAPTER 8, SECTION 4

Just the Facts Handout

Characteristics of an Oligopolistic Market

The three characteristics of an **oligopolistic market** are as follows:
1. The market has few sellers.
2. Firms produce and sell either identical products or slightly different products.
3. The barriers to entry are high. This means that it is difficult to enter the market.

Oligopolistic Firms Are Price Searchers

Like monopolistic and monopolistic competitive firms, oligopolistic firms are price searchers. They can raise the price of their good and still sell some of the good they produce.

How Much Competition Do Oligopolists Face?

A seller faces less competition the more unique its product is. It also faces less competition if it is more difficult for new sellers to enter the market.

An oligopolistic seller faces stiff competition from current sellers because its product is not very unique. An oligopolistic seller does not face too much competition from potential sellers because it is difficult to enter an oligopolistic market.

Identifying Oligopolistic Industries

Economists determine whether a market is oligopolistic by looking at the percentage of sales that goes to different firms in the industry. If a large percentage of sales goes to the top four firms, then the market is considered oligopolistic.

Oligopoly and Interdependence: Looking over Your Shoulder

Oligopoly differs from other market structures in terms of the number of sellers. Only an oligopolistic market consists of *few* sellers. When there are few sellers, each one tends to behave like the other sellers do. For example, the airline market is considered oligopolistic. If one airline lowers its ticket prices, other airlines are likely to do the same.

Cartels

A **cartel agreement** says that firms will work together to reduce the competition and raise profits. In the United States, cartel agreements are illegal. But even if they were legal, they probably would not be much of a problem for consumers. Firms that enter into cartel agreements usually end up breaking them.

Price Discrimination

Price discrimination exists when a seller charges different prices to different buyers and the price differences do not reflect cost differences. Suppose a movie theater charges children $4 to see a movie and charges adults $8 to see a movie. Also suppose that it does not cost the theater more to show the movie to adults. In this case, the theater is practicing price discrimination.

Price discrimination is one way of increasing revenue. Every seller wants to price discriminate to increase total revenue. However, not every seller can do so. Three conditions must be present before a seller can price discriminate:

1. Different customers must be willing and able to pay different prices for a good.
2. The seller needs a way to tell who is willing to pay more for the same good.
3. It must be impossible, or extremely costly, for customers to resell the good.

Price discrimination is illegal in the United States under certain conditions. It is illegal if it hurts competition. It is also usually illegal if it crosses state lines. For example, it is illegal to sells a good for less in one state than in another state unless it is more expensive to offer the good in the other state.

Price discrimination is not usually illegal if it does not hurt competition. It is also not usually illegal if the seller can show that it needs to charge a lower price to some customers in order to compete in the market.

Answer questions 1–4 in the Section 4 Assessment on page 241 of your textbook.

CHAPTER 8

Graphic Organizer Activity

Supply the missing words in the blank spaces of this graphic organizer.

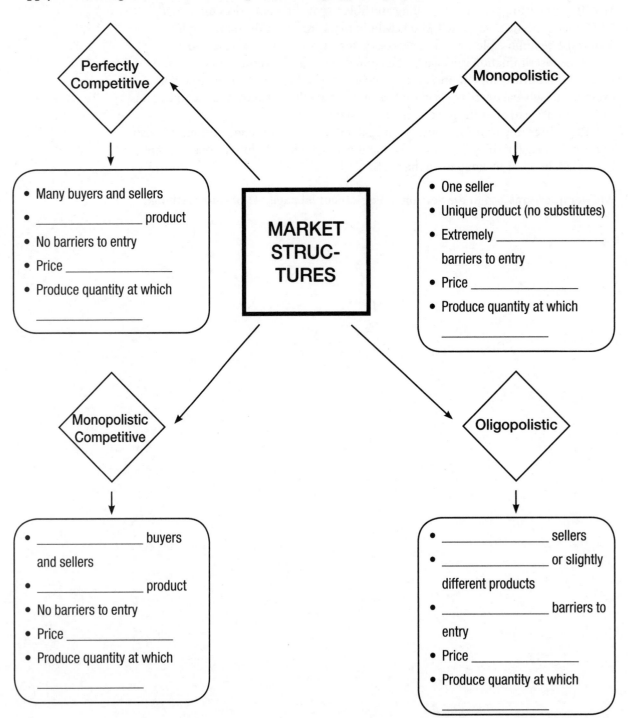

Perfectly Competitive

- Many buyers and sellers
- _____ product
- No barriers to entry
- Price _____
- Produce quantity at which _____

Monopolistic

- One seller
- Unique product (no substitutes)
- Extremely _____ barriers to entry
- Price _____
- Produce quantity at which _____

MARKET STRUC-TURES

Monopolistic Competitive

- _____ buyers and sellers
- _____ product
- No barriers to entry
- Price _____
- Produce quantity at which _____

Oligopolistic

- _____ sellers
- _____ or slightly different products
- _____ barriers to entry
- Price _____
- Produce quantity at which _____

CHAPTER 8
Vocabulary Activity

For each question, fill in the blank with the correct term from the following list.

market structure
perfectly competitive market
price taker
monopolistic market
barrier to entry
price searcher
public franchise

natural monopoly
antitrust law
monopolistic competitive market
oligopolistic market
cartel agreement
price discrimination

1. A right granted to a firm by government that permits the firm to provide a particular good or service and excludes all others from doing so is a(n) _____.

2. A(n) _____ is a seller that can sell some of its output at various prices.

3. A firm with such a low average total cost (per-unit cost) that only it can survive in the market is a(n) _____.

4. In a(n) _____, there are many buyers and many sellers, firms produce and sell slightly differentiated products, and firms have easy entry into and exit out of the market.

5. _____ is the practice by which a seller charges different prices (to different buyers) for the product it sells when the price differences do not reflect cost differences.

6. A market structure in which there are few sellers, firms produce and sell either identical or slightly differentiated products, and the barriers to entry are significant is a(n) _____.

7. A(n) _____ is legislation passed for the stated purpose of controlling monopoly power and preserving and promoting competition.

8. Anything that prohibits a firm from entering a market is a(n) _____.

9. A(n) _____ specifies how the firms that entered into the agreement will act in a coordinated way to reduce the competition among them.

10. The setting in which a seller finds itself is its _____.

11. A seller that can sell all its output at the equilibrium price but can sell none of its output at any other price is a(n) _____.

12. In a(n) _____, there are many buyers and many sellers, all firms sell identical goods, buyers and sellers have all relevant information about buying and selling activities, and firms have easy entry into and exit out of the market.

13. A market structure in which there is a single seller, the seller sells a product that has no close substitutes, and barriers to entry are high is a(n) _____.

CHAPTER 8

Working with Graphs and Tables Activity

Complete the following table that compares the four major market structures.

Characteristic	Perfectly competitive market	Monopolistic competitive market	Oligopolistic market	Monopolistic market
Number of sellers				
Type of product				
Barriers to entry				
Control over price				
Example of a firm				

CHAPTER 8

Practice Test

True or False

For each of these statements, place a T in the blank if the statement is true or an F if the statement is false.

1. _____ A natural monopoly is a right granted to a firm by government that permits the firm to provide a particular good or service and excludes all others from doing so.

2. _____ A government monopoly is legally protected from competition.

3. _____ A monopoly firm is a price taker.

4. _____ Firms in an oligopolistic market act in an interdependent way.

5. _____ Firms in a perfectly competitive market can sell all of their output at the market equilibrium price.

6. _____ A monopolistic competitive firm can gain higher profits if it can differentiate its product from its competition.

7. _____ A cartel is a group of firms that agree to act as perfect competitors.

8. _____ Oligopolistic firms are price searchers because they may sell identical products and entry into the market is easy.

9. _____ A perfectly competitive firm can increase its profits by selling its product for less than equilibrium price.

10. _____ If a monopoly firm earns profits, firms outside the market will enter the market and take away some of those profits.

11. _____ A monopoly searches for the highest possible price to charge buyers.

12. _____ A monopolistic firm produces and sells 50 units of a good at a price of $5 per unit. Its total cost is $300. The firm's profit is $50.

13. _____ You find out that every gas station in your city sells gas at the same price per gallon. Based on this information alone, it is *not* correct to say that the gas stations have definitely formed a cartel.

Short Answer

Write your answers on the lines provided.

1. Why do cartels tend to occur in oligopolistic markets and not in perfectly competitive markets?

   _____

   _____

   _____

2. Cartels are illegal in the United States. What happens to price when a cartel is broken up?

   _____

   _____

   _____

3. Why won't a monopoly charge the highest possible price?

   _____

   _____

   _____

CHAPTER 9, SECTION 1

Outlining Activity

Look through the chapter for an overview of the material. Pay attention to the main topics in the book. As you scan each section of the book, fill in the missing words in the following outline.

I. Supply and Demand in the Labor Market

    A. Employers are the people who _____ labor.

    B. Employees are the people who _____ labor.

    C. The price of labor is the _____.

II. How the Equilibrium Wage Rate Is Established

    A. The equilibrium wage rate is the wage at which the _____ of labor equals the _____ of labor.

    B. If the _____ of labor is greater than the _____ of labor, the market has a surplus of labor.

> Surplus of labor → Wage rate _____

    C. If the _____ of labor is greater than the _____ of labor, the market has a shortage of labor.

> Shortage of labor → Wage rate _____

III. Why Do Some People Earn More than Others?

    A. Wage rates can differ because the supply of different types of labor is not the same.

    B. Wage rates can differ because the _____ for different types of labor is not the same.

IV. Are Money Benefits the Only Thing That Matters?

    A. All jobs come with both money benefits and _____ benefits.

> Benefits in a job = Money benefits (income) + _____ benefits

    Guided Reading and Study Guide   © EMC Publishing

V. The Demand for a Good and Wage Rates

A. If the demand for the good that labor produces falls, the demand for workers _____ and the wage rate _____.

B. The demand for labor is a(n) _____ demand. It depends on the demand for the good or service that labor produces.

VI. What Will You Earn?

A. The greater the demand for the product you produce, the _____ is the demand for your labor services.

B. The more productive you are at what you do, the _____ the demand for you.

C. The fewer people who can do what you do, the _____ your wage will be.

VII. Government and the Minimum Wage

A. The _____ law sets a wage floor, or a level below which hourly wage rates are not allowed to fall.

B. A minimum wage rate set above the equilibrium wage rate will result in employers being willing and able to hire _____ workers.

VIII. Two Types of Wages: Nominal and Real

A. _____ wage is a person's wage in terms of actual money, or dollars.

B. _____ wage is a person's wage in terms of what it buys.

C. A(n) _____ is the "average price" of a variety of goods.

D. The _____, or CPI, is a common price index.

E. The real wage equals the nominal wage in a given year divided by the _____ in the same year.

CHAPTER 9, SECTION 1

Just the Facts Handout

Supply and Demand in the Labor Market

Supply and demand can be used to analyze how we determine the price of a resource, or factor of production, such as labor. People who demand labor are usually referred to as employers. People who supply labor are employees. Looking at employers and employees in this way, we can create a demand curve and a supply curve showing the price of labor. The price of labor is the **wage rate**. (See Exhibits 9-1 and 9-2 on page 247 of your textbook.)

How the Equilibrium Wage Rate Is Established

In the labor market, the equilibrium wage rate is the wage at which the quantity demanded of labor equals the quantity supplied of labor.

If the number of people who are willing and able to work (quantity supplied) is greater than the number of people employers are willing and able to hire (quantity demanded), the market has a surplus of labor. When the market has a surplus of labor, the wage rate falls.

If the number of people employers are willing and able to hire (quantity demanded) is greater than the number of people who are willing and able to work (quantity supplied), the market has a shortage of labor. When the market has a shortage of labor, the wage rate rises.

If the number of people who are willing and able to work (quantity supplied) equals the number of people employers are willing and able to hire (quantity demanded), the market has neither a surplus nor a shortage of labor. The wage rate neither rises nor falls at this equilibrium wage rate. (See Exhibit 9-3 on page 248 of your textbook.)

Why Do Some People Earn More than Others?

Wage rates can differ because the supply of different types of labor is not the same. Wage rates can also differ because the demand for different types of labor is not the same.

Are Money Benefits the Only Thing That Matters?

A higher income (more money per year) earned at a job is not the only thing that matters to people. Nonmoney benefits are also important. These benefits include what people are doing in their jobs, who their coworkers are, where they work, how many hours a week they work, and how much vacation time they receive. Benefits in a job equal money benefits (income) plus nonmoney benefits.

For example, suppose job A pays $10,000 more than job B. Also suppose the nonmoney benefits of job B are worth at least $10,000 more than the nonmoney benefits of job A. A person would choose job B even though she or he would earn less income (money benefits).

The Demand for a Good and Wage Rates

If the demand for a good falls, the demand for the workers who produce the good will fall. The wage rate for these workers will also fall.

Because the demand for labor depends on the demand for the good or service labor produces, the demand for labor is often referred to as a **derived demand**. A derived demand is a demand that is the result of some other demand.

What Will You Earn?

The higher the demand for your labor services, the higher your wage rate will be. Two factors will make the demand for your labor services high:
1. the demand for the good you produce
2. your productivity

The greater the demand for the product you produce, the greater the demand for your labor services. The more productive you are at what you do, the greater the demand for you.

The wage you earn also depends on supply. All other things being equal, the fewer people there are who can do what you do, the higher your wage (or salary) will be.

Government and the Minimum Wage

The **minimum wage law** sets a wage floor. A wage floor is a level below which hourly wage rates are not allowed to fall. What will happen if Congress sets a minimum wage rate that is higher than the equilibrium wage rate? Employers will be willing and able to hire fewer workers.

Two Types of Wages: Nominal and Real

We can measure a person's wage rate in terms of money—for example, $9 or $11 an hour. Measuring a person's wage rate in terms of money gives us the person's *nominal wage*. We can also measure a person's wage rate in terms of what the wages will buy. Measuring a person's wage rate in terms of what the wages will buy gives us the person's *real wage*.

The government measures the "average price" of a variety of goods. This average is usually called a price index. One well-known price index is the consumer price index, or CPI. The government computes the CPI on an annual basis. Therefore, we can compute our real wage by simply dividing our nominal wage in a given year by the CPI in the same year.

Answer questions 1–5 in the Section 1 Assessment on page 257 of your textbook.

CHAPTER 9, SECTION 2
Outlining Activity

Look through the chapter for an overview of the material. Pay attention to the main topics in the book. As you scan each section of the book, fill in the missing words in the following outline.

I. Some Practices of Labor Unions

A. A labor union is an organization that seeks to increase the _____ and improve the _____ of its members.

B. Labor unions try to increase the _____ for union labor by increasing the demand for the _____ that union members produce.

C. Labor unions try to control the _____ of union labor.

   1. A(n) _____ is an organization that hires only union members. The Taft-Hartley Act made _____ illegal.

   2. A(n) _____ does not require individuals to be union members in order to be hired, but it requires employees to join the union within a certain period of time after being hired. Union shops are legal in some states.

   3. Twenty-two states have passed right-to-work laws. In these states, the union shop is illegal.

II. Unions' Effects on Union and Nonunion Wages

A. Most studies show that union labor earns _____ than comparable nonunion labor.

B. Unions can increase the wage rate of union jobs. For example, if some union workers are laid off and seek employment in the nonunion market, the wages will lower in the nonunion market as supply of labor increases.

III. Two Views of Labor Unions

A. The _____ view says that labor unions are an obstacle to establishing reasonable work standards and make employers less _____.

B. A newer view says that labor unions are a collective voice for their members.

   1. Evidence in some industries indicates that union firms have a higher rate of _____ than nonunion firms.

   2. A labor union plays a role as a _____ mechanism for its members.

3. Without a labor union, disgruntled workers may feel taken advantage of by their employers, or feel unsafe in their work, and may leave their jobs and seek work elsewhere.

4. The labor union makes employees feel more confident, less intimidated, and more secure in their work.

IV. A Brief History of the Labor Movement

A. The _____ was organized in 1869. It welcomed anyone who worked for a living—farmers, skilled workers, and unskilled workers—with a few exceptions.

B. The _____ (AFL) was formed in 1886 under the leadership of Samuel Gompers, who ran the organization until his death in 1924. Gompers believed that the AFL should consist mainly of _____ workers.

C. In the early days of the labor union movement, the courts treated unions as _____ conspiracies.

D. The _____ Act of 1932 declared that workers should be "free from the interference, restraint, or coercion of employers" in choosing their union representatives.

E. The _____ Act of 1935 required employers to bargain in good faith with workers.

F. The _____ unionized the steel, rubber, textile, meatpacking, and automobile industries along industrial union lines.

G. In 1955, the AFL, a craft union, and the CIO, an industrial union, merged into the _____.

H. The _____ Act of 1947 gave states the right to pass right-to-work laws.

I. The _____ Act of 1959 called for regular union elections and secret ballots and required union leaders to report on their unions' finances. It also prohibited ex-convicts and communists from holding union office.

J. Members of a(n) _____ union work for local, state, or the federal government. In the1960s and 1970s, there was sharp growth in this type of union membership.

V. Government Regulation

A. Government regulates labor markets in such areas as hiring practices and _____ regulations.

B. Some people argue that regulation is too costly to taxpayers. Others say that even though the costs are high, the _____ are higher.

C. Economists point out the benefits and costs of regulation and the sometimes _____.

CHAPTER 9, SECTION 2

Just the Facts Handout

Some Practices of Labor Unions

One objective of a **labor union** is to get higher pay for its members. To do this, the union tries to increase the demand for its labor, decrease the supply of its labor, or both.

The Demand for Union Labor

If the demand for a good increases, the demand for the workers who produce the good increases. For this reason, a labor union might try to increase the demand for the product its workers produce. For example, it might use ads to urge people to buy only goods made by union workers.

The Supply of Union Labor

The lower the supply of workers used to produce a good, the higher the wage rate for the workers, if all other things remain the same. In the past, some unions supported **closed shops**. To work for these companies, people would first have to join a labor union. The labor union might limit the number of workers who could join. Unions would do this in order to keep the supply of workers in the industry low and to keep wage rates high. Today, the closed shop is prohibited by the **Taft-Hartley Act** of 1947.

In contrast, **union shops** are legal in many states. A union shop does not require individuals to join a union before they can be hired. However, it does require employees to join a union within a certain period of time after they are hired. Labor unions like union shops because they increase the number of union members in their industries. If everyone in a particular trade or industry is a member of a union, it is easier for the union to control the supply of labor. One way unions control the supply of labor is through strikes. In a **strike**, union members stop working in order to put pressure on an employer.

Today, 24 states have passed right-to-work laws. A **right-to-work law** makes it illegal to require employees to join a union. In short, it makes the union shop illegal.

Unions' Effects on Union and Nonunion Wages

From 1920 to 1979, the average wage of union members was 10 to 15 percent higher than the average wage of nonunion employees. Unions can affect the wages of both union and nonunion workers.

Two Views of Labor Unions

There are basically two views of labor unions: the traditional view, and a newer view. The traditional view holds that labor unions make it difficult to establish reasonable work standards. Therefore, they make companies less competitive.

The newer view says that the labor union is a valuable collective voice for its members. It appears that in some industries, union firms are more productive than nonunion firms. Without a labor union unhappy workers leave their jobs and look for work elsewhere. This "job exiting" raises training costs for the firm. It also results in long periods during which those searching for jobs are not producing goods. Overall, the labor union makes employees feel happier in their work. Such positive feelings usually mean more productive employees.

A Brief History of the Labor Movement

The United States began to move toward unionism after the Civil War. A number of key events have marked the progress of this movement.

The Knights of Labor was organized in 1869. The Knights of Labor welcomed almost anyone who worked for a living. The group called for higher wages and an eight-hour working day.

The American Federation of Labor (AFL) was formed in 1886. Samuel Gompers led its formation. He believed that the AFL should consist mainly of skilled workers.

In the early days of the labor union movement, the courts treated unions as illegal conspiracies. Union leaders were regularly charged with crimes and sued for damages. This changed dramatically in 1932 when the Norris-LaGuardia Act was passed. This act declared that workers were free to choose their own union representatives.

In 1935, Congress passed the Wagner Act. This act required employers to bargain in good faith with workers. The act also made it illegal for employers to interfere with their employees' rights to organize or join a union. In addition, the act set up the National Labor Relations Board (NLRB). The NLRB was established to investigate unfair labor practices. Union membership grew by leaps and bounds as a result of the Norris-LaGuardia and Wagner Acts.

In 1938, John L. Lewis of the United Mine Workers broke with the AFL and formed the Congress of Industrial Organizations (CIO). The CIO successfully unionized the steel, rubber, textile, meatpacking, and automobile industries.

After World War II, membership in the CIO began to decline. Some thought that bickering between the AFL and the CIO was the cause. In 1955, the AFL, a craft union, and the CIO, an industrial union, merged under the leadership of George Meany into the AFL-CIO.

Congress's attitude toward unions began to shift after World War II. A few particularly damaging strikes in 1946 set the stage for the Taft-Hartley Act in 1947. This act gave states the right to pass right-to-work laws. Such laws stated that employees could not be required to join a union.

Congress passed the Landrum-Griffin Act of 1959. This act controls the internal affairs of labor unions. It calls for regular union elections and secret ballots. It requires union leaders to report on their unions' finances. It also prohibits former convicts and communists from holding union office.

A public employee union is a union whose members work for local, state, or the federal government. The most important development in the labor movement in the 1960s and 1970s was the sharp growth in membership in public employee unions.

Government Regulation

Government regulates labor markets with regard to such issues as hiring practices and safety regulations. Not everyone agrees as to the value of government regulation. Some people argue that regulation is too costly. Others say that the benefits are greater than the costs. Economists point out both the costs and benefits of regulation. They also point out the unintended effects that sometimes occur with regulation.

Answer questions 1–6 in the Section 2 Assessment on page 269 of your textbook.

CHAPTER 9

Graphic Organizer Activity

Supply the missing words in the blank spaces of these graphic organizers.

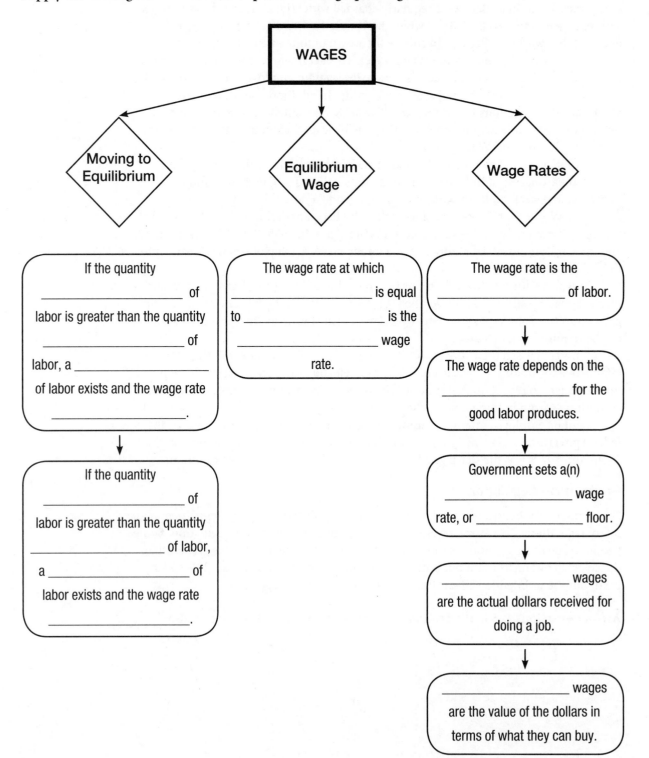

WAGES

Moving to Equilibrium

Equilibrium Wage

Wage Rates

If the quantity _____ of labor is greater than the quantity _____ of labor, a _____ of labor exists and the wage rate _____.

If the quantity _____ of labor is greater than the quantity _____ of labor, a _____ of labor exists and the wage rate _____.

The wage rate at which _____ is equal to _____ is the _____ wage rate.

The wage rate is the _____ of labor.

The wage rate depends on the _____ for the good labor produces.

Government sets a(n) _____ wage rate, or _____ floor.

_____ wages are the actual dollars received for doing a job.

_____ wages are the value of the dollars in terms of what they can buy.

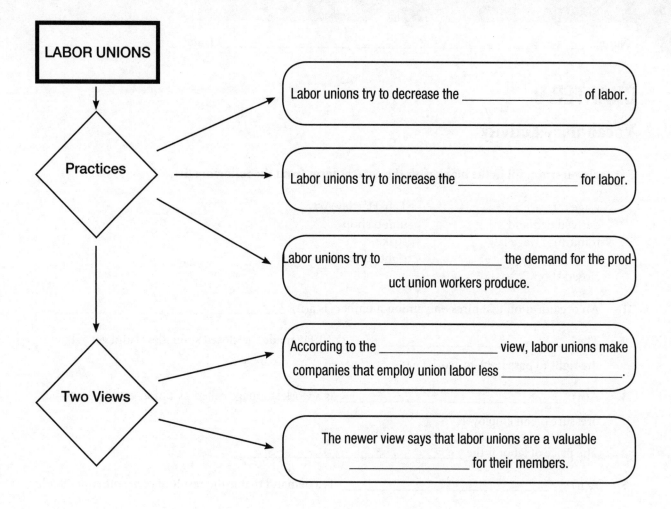

LABOR UNIONS

Practices

Labor unions try to decrease the _____ of labor.

Labor unions try to increase the _____ for labor.

Labor unions try to _____ the demand for the product union workers produce.

Two Views

According to the _____ view, labor unions make companies that employ union labor less _____.

The newer view says that labor unions are a valuable _____ for their members.

CHAPTER 9
Vocabulary Activity

For each question, fill in the blank with the correct term from the following list.

wage rate	Taft-Hartley Act
derived demand	union shop
minimum wage law	strike
labor union	right-to-work law
closed shop	

1. An organization that hires only union members is a(n) _____.

2. The _____ of 1947 made the closed shop illegal and gave states the right to pass right-to-work laws.

3. A(n) _____ is a work stoppage called by union employees to put pressure on an employer.

4. The price of labor is the _____.

5. A(n) _____ is a demand that is the result of some other demand.

6. A(n) _____ is a state law that prohibits the practice of requiring employees to join a union in order to work.

7. A(n) _____ is a federal law that specifies the lowest hourly wage rate that can be paid to workers.

8. A(n) _____ is an organization that requires employees to join the union within a certain period after being hired.

9. A(n) _____ is an organization that seeks to increase the wages and improve the working conditions of its members.

CHAPTER 9

Working with Graphs and Tables Activity

The following time line shows the history of the labor movement in the United States. Fill in the missing words in the time line.

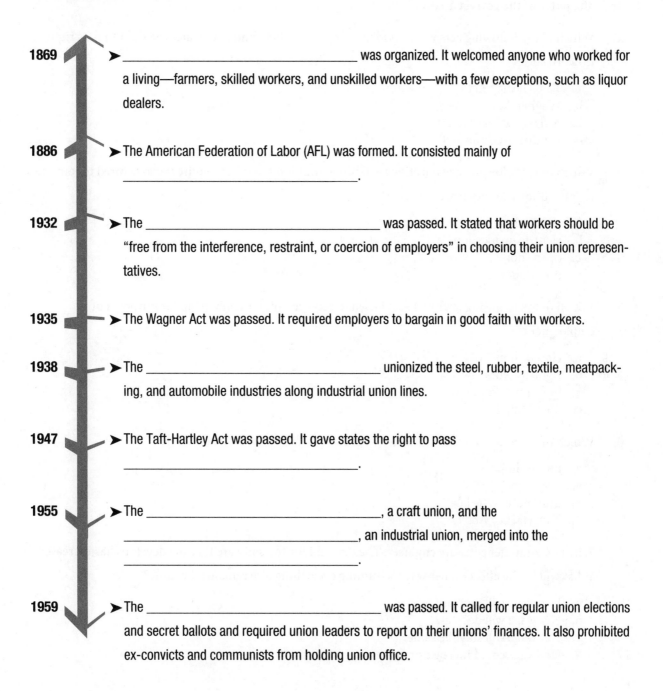

1869 → _____ was organized. It welcomed anyone who worked for a living—farmers, skilled workers, and unskilled workers—with a few exceptions, such as liquor dealers.

1886 → The American Federation of Labor (AFL) was formed. It consisted mainly of _____.

1932 → The _____ was passed. It stated that workers should be "free from the interference, restraint, or coercion of employers" in choosing their union representatives.

1935 → The Wagner Act was passed. It required employers to bargain in good faith with workers.

1938 → The _____ unionized the steel, rubber, textile, meatpacking, and automobile industries along industrial union lines.

1947 → The Taft-Hartley Act was passed. It gave states the right to pass _____.

1955 → The _____, a craft union, and the _____, an industrial union, merged into the _____.

1959 → The _____ was passed. It called for regular union elections and secret ballots and required union leaders to report on their unions' finances. It also prohibited ex-convicts and communists from holding union office.

CHAPTER 9

Practice Test

Multiple Choice

Circle the letter of the correct answer.

1. Which of the following acts was passed by Congress in 1947 and gave states the right to pass right-to-work laws?

   a. Taft-Hartley Act
   b. Wagner Act
   c. Norris-LaGuardia Act
   d. Landrum-Griffin Act

2. Which of the following organizations will hire nonunion labor but require persons hired to join the union within a certain period of time?

   a. closed shop
   b. right-to-work shop
   c. open shop
   d. union shop

3. Which of the following laws makes it illegal to require union membership for purposes of employment?

   a. closed shop law
   b. right-to-work law
   c. minimum wage law
   d. open shop law

4. Which of the following does not allow wage rates to fall below a certain level?

   a. union shop
   b. closed shop
   c. minimum wage law
   d. Taft-Hartley Act

5. Sally is a computer software engineer. The demand for the software that she develops has increased. What will be the effect on her wage, assuming everything else remains the same?

   a. Her wage will increase.
   b. Her wage will decrease.
   c. Her wage will stay the same.
   d. Her wage could increase or decrease.

6. Suppose the minimum wage rate is higher than the equilibrium wage rate. Which of the following is most likely to occur?

   a. Fewer people will end up working at the minimum wage rate than would like to work.
   b. Everyone who wants a job will find a job.
   c. More people will be hired than would be without the minimum wage.
   d. Worker productivity will increase.

7. If the demand for labor increases by the same amount as the supply of labor increases, what will happen to wages?

   a. Wages will rise.
   b. Wages will fall.
   c. Wages will remain the same.
   d. Wages could rise or fall.

8. If the demand for labor increases by less than the supply of labor increases, what will happen to wages?

   a. Wages will rise.
   b. Wages will fall.
   c. Wages will remain the same.
   d. Wages could rise or fall.

9. Joe earns $50,000 at his present job. Another company offered Joe a job that paid $75,000, but he turned down the offer. The nonmoney benefits in the lower-paying job equal at least what dollar amount?

   a. $50,000
   b. $25,000
   c. $75,000
   d. $125,000

10. In a competitive labor market, suppose quantity demanded of labor is less than the quantity supplied. What will happen to the wage rate?

   a. The wage rate will rise.
   b. The wage rate will fall.
   c. The wage rate will remain the same.
   d. The wage rate could rise or fall.

Short Answer

Write your answers on the lines provided.

1. The number of high school students in California is expected to increase by a large amount in the next few years. Use the concept of derived demand for labor to explain how this increase in students could affect teachers' wages.

   _____

   _____

   _____

2. Why do professional athletes earn so much money? Explain your answer using the concepts of the demand for and supply of labor.

   _____

   _____

   _____

CHAPTER 10, SECTION 1

Outlining Activity

Look through the chapter for an overview of the material. Pay attention to the main topics in the book. As you scan each section of the book, fill in the missing words in the following outline.

I. What's It Like Living in a Barter Economy?

    A. A(n) _____ economy is an economy with no money. _____ are made in goods and services instead of in money.

    B. The _____ costs of making exchanges are high in a barter economy.

II. How and Why Did Money Come to Exist?

    A. Money is any good that is widely _____ in exchange and in the payment of debts.

    B. Some goods that evolved into money were gold, silver, copper, rocks, cattle, and shells.

III. What Gives Money Value?

    A. General acceptability in exchange gives money its value.

IV. Are You Better Off Living in a Money Economy?

    A. The transaction costs of exchange are _____ in a money economy than in a barter economy.

    B. _____ transaction costs mean _____ time is needed to make exchanges in a money economy than in a barter economy.

    C. This extra time can be used to _____ more goods and services, to _____ more _____, or to do both.

    D. The residents of money economies are _____ in goods, services, and leisure than the residents of _____ economies.

    E. The residents of money economies are more _____ because transaction costs are _____. People can _____ in producing one thing, selling that one thing for money, and then using the money to buy other goods and services.

V. What Are the Three Functions of Money?

A. Money functions as a(n) _____ of exchange. A(n) _____ of exchange is anything that is generally acceptable in exchange for goods and services.

B. Money functions as a(n) _____. A(n) _____ is a common measurement (dollars, for example) used to express values.

C. Money functions as a(n) _____. A good is a(n) _____ if it maintains its value over time.

VI. Who Were the Early Bankers?

A. When money was principally _____ coins, carrying it was neither easy nor safe. So individuals wanted to store their _____ in a safe place.

B. Individuals turned to _____ because they were already equipped with safe storage facilities. _____ were the first bankers.

C. _____ issued _____ receipts to their customers to acknowledge the amount of _____ stored.

D. People began to circulate the warehouse receipts in place of the gold itself. The warehouse receipts circulated as _____. At this stage, warehouse receipts were _____ backed by gold.

E. Goldsmiths began to lend out some of the gold deposited with them and collected _____ on the loans.

F. The lending activity of goldsmiths increased the _____ of money as measured by the number of warehouse receipts compared to the actual amount of gold. This process was the beginning of _____ reserve banking.

CHAPTER 10, SECTION 1

Just the Facts Handout

What's It Like Living in a Barter Economy?

A **barter economy** is an economy with no money. The only way you can get what you want in a barter economy is to trade something you have for it. Living in a barter economy is difficult because many of the people you want to trade with don't want to trade with you.

In this situation, trade is time consuming. Economists state the problem this way: the **transaction costs** of making exchanges are high in a barter economy. Think of transaction costs as the time and effort you have to spend before you can make an exchange.

How and Why Did Money Come to Exist?

When a good is widely accepted in exchange, the good is called money. **Money** is any good that is widely accepted in exchange and in the repayment of debts. Historically, goods that evolved into money included gold, silver, copper, rocks, cattle, and shells.

What Gives Money Value?

Our money has value because people generally accept it. Money has value to you because you know that you can use it to get what you want. However, you can use money to get what you want only because other people will accept it in exchange for what they have.

Are You Better Off Living in a Money Economy?

The transaction costs of exchange are lower in a money economy than in a barter economy. In a barter economy, not everyone you want to trade with wants to trade with you. In a money economy, everyone you want to trade with wants what you have— money. In short, transaction costs are lower when others are willing to trade with you.

Lower transaction costs mean that you need less time to trade. Using money frees up some time for you. With that extra time, you can produce more of whatever you produce, consume more leisure, or do both. In a money economy, people produce more goods and services and consume more leisure than they would in a barter economy. People who live in money economies are richer in goods, services, and leisure than the residents of barter economies.

People who live in money economies also do more specialized work because transaction costs are low. Instead of spending time bartering, they can focus on producing one thing. They can then sell that one thing for money, and use the money to buy other goods and services.

What Are the Three Functions of Money?

Money has three major functions. It serves as
1. a medium of exchange;
2. a unit of account; and
3. a store of value

A **medium of exchange** is anything that is generally acceptable in exchange for goods and services. A **unit of account** is a common measurement used to express values. Money functions as a unit of account because all goods can be expressed in terms of money. A good is a **store of value** if it maintains its value over time. Money maintains its value over time. For example, you can sell your labor services today, collect money in payment, and spend the money on goods and services tomorrow.

Who Were the Early Bankers?

When money was principally gold coins, carrying it was neither easy nor safe. As a result, people wanted to store their gold in a safe place. Most often, people stored their gold coins with goldsmiths because goldsmiths had safe storage facilities. Goldsmiths were the first bankers.

Goldsmiths gave their customers warehouse receipts stating the amount of gold stored. People began to use the warehouse receipts in place of the actual gold coins because it was easier to do so. In this way, warehouse receipts were used as money. At this stage, warehouse receipts were fully backed by gold. The receipts simply represented the actual stored gold.

Then, some goldsmiths began to lend out some of the gold they were storing, and collected interest on the loans. However, instead of lending the actual gold, the goldsmiths gave warehouse receipts to the borrowers. As a result, there were more receipts than there was actual gold.

The goldsmiths' lending activity increased the supply of money. That is, it increased the number of warehouse receipts compared with the actual amount of gold. This process was the beginning of **fractional reserve banking**. Under fractional reserve banking, banks are like the goldsmiths of years past. They hold only a fraction of their deposits and lend out the remainder.

Answer questions 1–4 in the Section 1 Assessment on page 284 of your textbook.

CHAPTER 10, SECTION 2

Outlining Activity

Look through the chapter for an overview of the material. Pay attention to the main topics in the book. As you scan each section of the book, fill in the missing words in the following outline.

I. **What Are the Components of the Money Supply?**

   A. The most basic money supply in the United States—called M1—is composed of

   _____, _____, and _____.

   B. Currency includes _____ minted by the U.S. Treasury and

   _____.

   C. Checking accounts are accounts in which funds are deposited and can be withdrawn simply

   by writing a(n) _____. Checking accounts are also referred to as

   _____ because the funds can be converted to currency on demand and

   given to the person to whom the check is made payable.

   D. _____ are checks issued by a bank and sold to a traveler (or to anyone who

   wishes to buy them). The purchaser signs the checks at the time they are issued by the bank. The

   purchaser then signs a check again in the presence of the person cashing it.

   E. In February 2017, $1,433 billion in currency was in circulation, $1,936 billion in checking

   accounts, and $3 billion in traveler's checks. The money supply was _____.

II. **Moving Beyond M1 to M2**

   A. _____ is a broader measure of money supply.

   B. A savings account is a(n) _____ account.

   C. A time deposit is an interest-earning deposit with a specified maturity date.

   D. A money market deposit account (MMDA) is an interest-earning account that usually requires

   a(n) _____.

   E. A money market mutual fund (MMMF) is the same thing as a(n) _____,

   except it is with a mutual fund company.

III. Are Credit Cards Money?

A. A credit card is not money. It is a piece of plastic that allows the holder to take out a loan from the bank that issued the card.

B. The use of a credit card places a person in _____, which he or she then has to repay with money.

IV. Borrowing, Lending, and Interest Rates

A. Often, when loans are made, an interest rate must be paid for the loan.

B. Interest rates are determined in the _____ funds market.

C. The loanable funds market includes a(n) _____ for loans and a(n) _____ of loans.

D. The demanders of loans are called _____. The suppliers of loans are called _____.

E. The interaction of the demand for and supply of loans determines the interest rate (the price of the loan).

   1. If the demand for loans rises and the supply remains constant, the interest rate _____.

   2. If the demand for loans falls and the supply remains constant, the interest rate _____.

   3. If the supply for loans rises and the demand remains constant, the interest rate _____.

   4. If the supply for loans falls and the demand remains constant, the interest rate _____.

CHAPTER 10, SECTION 2

Just the Facts Handout

What Are the Components of the Money Supply?

The most basic **money supply** is often referred to as M1 (M-one). M1 consists of currency, checking accounts, and traveler's checks.

Currency includes both coins and paper money. Coins, such as quarters and dimes, are minted by the U.S. Treasury. Paper money consists of **Federal Reserve notes**. Federal Reserve notes are issued by the Federal Reserve System.

Checking accounts are accounts in which funds are deposited and from which funds can be withdrawn simply by writing a check. Sometimes checking accounts are referred to as **demand deposits**. This is because the person receiving a check can demand that the bank give him or her currency for the amount of the check. For example, suppose Malcolm has a balance of $400 in his checking account. He can take up to $400 currency out of his account. He can also transfer up to $400 to someone else by simply writing a check to that person.

A traveler's check is a check written by a bank and sold to a traveler or to anyone who wishes to buy it.

In February 2017, $1,433 billion in currency was in circulation, along with $1,936 billion in checking accounts, and $2 billion in traveler's checks. Altogether, the money supply equaled $3,371 billion. (See Exhibit 10-2 on page 286 of your textbook.)

Moving Beyond M1 to M2

M1 is the narrowest definition of money supply. M2 is a broader measure and includes everything in M1 plus savings deposits, small-denomination time deposits, money market deposit accounts, and retail money market mutual fund accounts.

A **savings account** is an interest-earning account. Some savings accounts have check-writing privileges; others do not.

A time deposit is an interest-earning deposit with a specified maturity date. Time deposits are subject to penalties for early withdrawal.

A money market deposit account (MMDA) is an interest-earning account that usually requires a minimum balance. Most MMDAs offer limited check-writing privileges.

A money market mutual fund (MMMF) is essentially the same thing as an MMDA, except it is with a mutual fund company. Only retail MMMFs are part of M2.

Are Credit Cards Money?

Money has to be widely accepted for exchange and in the repayment of debt. A credit card is not used to repay debt. Rather, a credit card is used to create loans. Those loans place people in debt. To get out of debt, they have to repay the loans with money.

Borrowing, Lending, and Interest Rates

Often, when loans are made, they have to be repaid with interest. The amount of interest depends on the interest rate, which is a percentage of the loan. For example, a bank may charge 12 percent interest on loans used to purchase new cars.

Interest rates are determined in the **loanable funds market**. This market sets interest rates much like the apple market sets prices.

The loanable funds market includes a demand for loans and a supply of loans. The demanders of loans are called borrowers. The suppliers of loans are called lenders. The interest rate is determined through the interaction of the demand for and supply of loans.

If the demand for loans rises and the supply remains constant, the price of a loan rises. The price of a loan is the interest rate. If the demand for loans falls, the interest rate falls. If the supply of loans rises, the interest rate falls. If the supply of loans falls, the interest rate rises.

Answer questions 1–3 in the Section 2 Assessment on page 289 of your textbook.

CHAPTER 10, SECTION 3
Outlining Activity

Look through the chapter for an overview of the material. Pay attention to the main topics in the book. As you scan each section of the book, fill in the missing words in the following outline.

    I. What Is the Federal Reserve System?

        A. The Federal Reserve System (the Fed) is the _____ of the United States.

        B. The _____ of the Federal Reserve System controls and coordinates the Fed's activities.

            1. The board is made up of _____ members, each appointed to a(n) _____ term by the president of the United States with Senate approval.

            2. The president also designates one member as _____ of the _____ for a(n) _____ term.

        C. There are _____ Federal Reserve district banks.

        D. The _____ (FOMC) is the major policy-making group within the Fed.

            1. The FOMC has _____ members.

            2. _____ of the _____ members are members of the Board of Governors. The other five members come from among the _____ of the Federal Reserve district banks.

    II. What Does the Fed Do?

        A. _____ the money supply.

        B. _____ the economy with paper money (Federal Reserve notes).

            1. The notes are issued to the 12 Federal Reserve district banks, which keep the money on hand to meet the demands of the banks and the public.

        C. Hold bank _____.

        D. Provide _____.

            1. The _____ process is how funds change hands when checks are written.

        E. _____ member banks.

        F. Serve as the _____ for banks suffering cash management problems.

CHAPTER 10, SECTION 3

Just the Facts Handout

What Is the Federal Reserve System?

The **Federal Reserve System (the Fed)** began operation in 1914. The Fed is a central bank. This means that it is the chief authority on money in the country. Today, the principal components of the Federal Reserve System are the Board of Governors and the 12 Federal Reserve district banks.

Board of Governors

The **Board of Governors of the Federal Reserve System** controls and coordinates the Fed's activities. The board is made up of seven members. Each member is appointed to a 14-year term by the president of the United States with Senate approval. The president also names one member as chairperson of the board for a four-year term.

The 12 Federal Reserve District Banks

The United States is broken up into 12 Federal Reserve districts. Exhibit 10-3 on page 295 of your textbook shows the boundaries of these districts. Each district has a Federal Reserve district bank. Each district bank has a president.

An Important Committee: The FOMC

The major policy-making group within the Fed is the **Federal Open Market Committee (FOMC)**. The FOMC is made up of 12 members. Seven of the 12 members are the members of the Board of Governors. The remaining five members are presidents of the Federal Reserve district banks.

What Does the Fed Do?

The Fed has six major responsibilities:

1. The Fed controls the money supply.
2. The Fed supplies the economy with paper money, that is, Federal Reserve notes. Federal Reserve notes are printed at the Bureau of Engraving and Printing in Washington, D.C. The notes are issued to the 12 Federal Reserve district banks. These banks give the money to the public and to the banks in their district.
3. The Fed holds bank reserves in reserve accounts. You can think of **reserve accounts** as checking accounts. Each commercial bank that is a member of the Federal Reserve System has to have a reserve account with its Federal Reserve district bank. For example, a commercial bank in Durham, North Carolina, must have a reserve account with the fifth Federal Reserve district bank in Richmond, Virginia. (The locations of the 12 Federal Reserve district banks are shown in Exhibit 10-3 on page 295 of your textbook.)
4. The Fed provides check-clearing services. The process by which funds change hands when checks are written is called the check-clearing process. The Fed plays a major role in this process. An example helps explain how this process works. (See Exhibit 10-4 on page 296 of your textbook.)
   a. Harry writes a $1,000 check and sends it to Ursula.
   b. Ursula receives the check, takes it to her local bank, and deposits it into her checking account. The balance in her account rises by $1,000.

    c. Ursula's bank sends the check to its Federal Reserve district bank. The reserve bank increases the reserve account of Ursula's bank by $1,000 and decreases the reserve account of Harry's bank by $1,000.

    d. The reserve bank sends the check to Harry's bank, which then reduces the balance in Harry's checking account by $1,000.

5. The Fed supervises member banks. Without warning, the Fed can examine the books of member commercial banks. The Fed will look at what kind of loans a bank made, whether it followed bank regulations, how accurate its records are, and so on.

6. The Fed serves as the lender of last resort. This means that the Fed may lend banks money when no one else will.

Answer questions 1–4 in the Section 3 Assessment on page 297 of your textbook.

Name: _____ Date: _____

CHAPTER 10, SECTION 4
Outlining Activity

Look through the chapter for an overview of the material. Pay attention to the main topics in the book. As you scan each section of the book, fill in the missing words in the following outline.

I. Different Types of Reserves

A. A bank's total _____ is the sum of its deposits in its

_____ account at the Fed and its _____.

> Total reserves = Deposits in the reserve account at the Fed + Vault cash

    1. For example, if bank A has $10 million in its reserve account with the Fed and $2 million in

    its vault, then its total reserves equal _____ million.

    2. Total reserves can be divided into _____ reserves and

    _____ reserves.

B. _____ reserves are the amount of reserves a bank must hold against its

_____ account deposits as mandated by the Fed.

    1. The _____ is the percentage of a bank's checking account deposits that

    it must keep in the form of reserves—that is, as deposits in its reserve account at the Fed plus

    vault cash.

    2. Required reserves equal the _____ times _____

    deposits.

> Required reserves = Reserve requirement × Checking account deposits

C. Excess reserves equal _____ minus _____. Banks can

make _____ with their excess reserves.

> Excess reserves = Total reserves − Required reserves

II. How Banks Increase the Money Supply

A. Bank A gets a new checking account deposit.

    1. Suppose $1,000 appears to Fred. He opens a checking account at bank A and deposits the $1,000. Bank A places the $1,000 into its vault, which means it is part of its total reserves.

    2. Suppose that Fred's deposit is the only checking account deposit at bank A and that the Fed has set the reserve requirement at 10 percent. So bank A must keep

    _____ × _____ = _____ in required reserves.

    3. Bank A's excess reserves equal _____ total reserves minus

    _____ required reserves, or _____.

B. Bank A creates new _____ with its _____ reserves of $900.

    1. Suppose Alexi asks for a $900 loan from bank A, and her loan is approved.

    2. Banks give out loans in the form of checking account deposits. Bank A opens up a checking account for Alexi. The balance in the account is $900.

    3. The money supply equals currency plus checking account deposits plus traveler's checks. When bank A opens Alexi's checking account, _____ deposits have increased by $900. So, the _____ has increased by $900.

C. Alexi writes a $900 check for a TV.

    1. The owner of the electronics store deposits the check at bank B.

    2. Bank B must keep _____ as required reserves (the 10 percent reserve requirement times the $900 deposit).

    3. Bank B can lend the excess reserves of _____ ($900 − $90). If it does so, the money supply increases by _____.

D. The story continues in the same way with other banks.

E. A simple formula can be used to find the (maximum) change in the money supply.

> Change in money supply = (1 ÷ Reserve requirement) × Change in reserves of first bank

    1. The maximum change in the money supply brought about by Fred's $1,000 is

    _____ × _____ = _____.

    2. The $1,000 created by Fred ends up increasing the money supply by a specific multiple—in this case, a multiple of 10.

CHAPTER 10, SECTION 4

Just the Facts Handout

Different Types of Reserves

To understand how the money supply rises and falls, you need to know the different types of a bank's reserves.

1. A bank's **total reserves** are the sum of its deposits in its reserve account at the Fed and its vault cash. A bank's total reserves can be divided into two types: required reserves and excess reserves.

2. **Required reserves** are the funds that a bank must keep in its checking account at the Federal Reserve bank or in its vault as cash. The **reserve requirement** is the regulation that requires banks to keep a certain percentage of their checking account deposits in the form of reserves.

3. **Excess reserves** are any reserves beyond the required amount. Excess reserves are the difference between total reserves and required reserves. Banks can make loans with their excess reserves. For example, if a bank has excess reserves of $15 million, it can make loans of $15 million.

The following equations summarize the different types of reserves (see Exhibit 10-5 on page 299 of your textbook):

Total reserves = Deposits in the reserve account at the Fed + Vault cash
Required reserves = Reserve requirement × Checking account deposits
Excess reserves = Total reserves − Required reserves

How Banks Increase the Money Supply

The money supply is the sum of three components: currency (coins and paper money), checking account deposits, and traveler's checks. Banks can create checking account deposits (checkbook money). If they do create checking account money, they increase the money supply.

Creating Checking Account Deposits

Suppose Fred snaps his fingers and creates a $1,000 bill. He walks into bank A, opens up a checking account, and deposits the $1,000 into the checking account. (See entry [a] in Exhibit 10-6 on page 300 of your textbook.)

The bank places the $1,000 into its vault. The money is now part of total reserves. Because vault cash has increased by $1,000, total reserves have also increased by $1,000.

Fred's deposit is the only checking account deposit at bank A, and the Fed has set the reserve requirement at 10 percent. The required reserves equal the reserve requirement multiplied by checking account deposits. So, bank A's required reserves = 10 percent × $1,000 = $100. (See entry [b] in Exhibit 10-6.)

Currently, bank A has more than $100 in its vault. It has the $1,000 that Fred handed over to it. Excess reserves equal total reserves minus required reserves. So, bank A's excess reserves = $1,000 (total reserves) − $100 (required reserves) = $900. (See entry [c] in Exhibit 10-6.)

What Does the Bank Do with Excess Reserves?

Banks create new loans with excess reserves. Suppose Alexi walks into bank A and asks for a $900 loan. The loan is approved.

The loan officer opens up a checking account for Alexi and tells her that the balance is $900. (See entry [c] in Exhibit 10-6.) Banks give out loans in the form of checking account deposits. (This point is important to remember.)

Bank A has increased the money supply by $900. Remember that the money supply consists of currency plus checking account deposits plus traveler's checks. When bank A opens up a checking account for Alexi, the dollar amount of currency has not changed. The dollar amount of traveler's checks has also not changed. The only thing that has changed is the dollar amount of checking account deposits. Checking account deposits are $900 higher, so the money supply is $900 higher.

What Happens After a Loan Is Granted?

Alexi goes to a retail store and buys a $900 TV. She pays for the set by writing out a check for $900 drawn on bank A. She hands the check to the owner of the store, Roberto.

At the end of the business day, Roberto takes the check to bank B. Before Roberto arrives, checking account deposits in bank B equal zero. Roberto changes this situation by depositing the $900 into his checking account. (See entry [d] in Exhibit 10-6.)

Bank B sends the check to its Federal Reserve bank. The reserve bank increases the balance in bank B's reserve account by $900. At the same time, the reserve bank decreases the funds in bank A's reserve account by $900. Total reserves for bank B rise by $900. The checking account deposits at bank B rise to $900, too. (Again, see entry [d] in Exhibit 10-6.)

The reserve requirement is 10 percent. So, bank B has to keep $90 as required reserves. (See entry [e] in Exhibit 10-6.) Bank B can use the excess reserves ($810) to offer new loans or create new checking account deposits. (See entry [f] in Exhibit 10-6.) The story continues in the same way with banks C, D, E, and so on.

How Much Money Was Created?

As a result of Fred's $1,000 deposit, banks A, B, C, D, E, and so on, will create $9,000 in new loans or checking account deposits (money). (Again, see Exhibit 10-6 on page 300 of your textbook.) This $9,000 is new money. It did not exist before Fred snapped his fingers, created $1,000 out of thin air, and then deposited it into a checking account in bank A.

The facts can be summarized as follows:

1. Fred created $1,000 in new paper currency (money) out of thin air.
2. After Fred deposited the $1,000 in bank A, the banking system created $9,000 in additional checking account deposits (money).

The maximum change in the money supply can be found by dividing 1 by the reserve requirement and multiplying this amount by the change in reserves of the first bank. In the example involving Fred, the reserve requirement was 10 percent (0.10). The reserves of bank A changed by $1,000. So, the change in the money supply $= (1 \div 0.10) \times \$1,000 = \$10,000$. The $1,000 created by Fred increased the money supply by a multiple of 10.

Answer questions 1–3 in the Section 4 Assessment on page 303 of your textbook.

CHAPTER 10, SECTION 5
Outlining Activity

Look through the chapter for an overview of the material. Pay attention to the main topics in the book. As you scan each section of the book, fill in the missing words in the following outline.

I. **Changing the** _____ **Requirement**

    A. The Fed can increase or decrease the money supply by changing the _____.

> Lower reserve requirement → Money supply _____
>
> Raise reserve requirement → Money supply _____

II. _____ **Operations**

    A. A government security is a piece of paper promising to pay a certain dollar amount of money in the future. The Fed may buy government securities from any member of the public or sell them.

    B. When the Fed buys a government security, it is said to be conducting an _____. When it sells a government security, it is said to be conducting an _____.

    C. An open market purchase _____ the money supply. An open market sale _____ the money supply.

> Open market purchase → Money supply rises
>
> Open market sale → Money supply falls

III. **Changing the** _____

    A. The interest rate charged by a bank to lend money to another bank is called the _____.

    B. The interest rate charged by the Fed to lend money to a member bank is called the _____.

C. If the federal funds rate is _____ than the discount rate, bank A will borrow from bank B instead of from the Fed. If the discount rate is _____ than the federal funds rate, bank A will probably borrow from the Fed.

D. If bank A borrows from bank B, no new money enters the economy. But if bank A borrows from the Fed, the Fed creates new money in the process of granting the loan.

E. If the Fed _____ its discount rate relative to the federal funds rate and if banks then borrow from the Fed, the money supply will _____. If the Fed increases the discount rate, the money supply will _____.

> Lower the discount rate → Money supply rises
>
> Raise the discount rate → Money supply falls

V. The Federal Funds Target Rate

A. One of the ways the Fed can change the _____ is to set the federal funds rate target.

B. The federal funds rate target is exactly what it sounds like: it is the rate the Fed would like the federal funds rate to be.

VI. The Discretion of the Fed

A. The Fed has the power today to increase and decrease the money supply of the country by any amount, even a large amount.

B. Some economists argue that this kind of power can be _____. It would be better, they say, if the Fed had to abide by some _____.

VII. Gold Standard

A. A gold standard could be used as a monetary rule.

B. A gold standard would require the _____ to determine the price for gold and vow to buy and sell gold at that set price.

C. As the market price of gold goes up and down, so do the prices of other goods and services.

D. The gold standard would _____ the value of the dollar in terms of what a dollar can purchase.

CHAPTER 10, SECTION 5

Just the Facts Handout

Changing the Reserve Requirement

To understand how a change in the reserve requirement can change the money supply, consider three cases. In each case, the money supply is initially zero and $1,000 is created out of thin air. The difference in the three cases is the reserve requirement.

Case 1: Reserve requirement = 5%.
Change in money supply = $(1 \div 0.05) \times \$1,000 = \$20,000$.
Case 2: Reserve requirement = 10%.
Change in money supply = $(1 \div 0.10) \times \$1,000 = \$10,000$
Case 3: Reserve requirement = 20%.
Change in money supply = $(1 \div 0.20) \times \$1,000 = \$5,000$

The change in the money supply is the largest ($20,000) when the reserve requirement is 5 percent. The change in the money supply is the smallest ($5,000) when the reserve requirement is 20 percent. The smaller the reserve requirement, the bigger the change in the money supply.

Thus, the Fed can increase or decrease the money supply by changing the reserve requirement. If the Fed lowers the reserve requirement, the money supply rises. If the Fed raises the reserve requirement, the money supply falls.

Open Market Operations

The Federal Open Market Committee (FOMC) conducts open market operations. **Open market operations** are the buying and selling of government securities by the Fed. The Fed may buy government securities from any member of the public. The Fed may also sell government securities to any member of the public. When the Fed buys a government security, it is said to be conducting an open market purchase. When the Fed sells a government security, it is said to be conducting an open market sale.

Open Market Purchases

Let's say that you own a government security. The Fed offers to purchase the security from you for $10,000. You agree to sell your security to the Fed. You hand it over, and you receive a check for $10,000.

You take the $10,000 check to your local bank and deposit it in your checking account. The total dollar amount of checking account deposits in the economy is now $10,000 more than it was before the Fed purchased your government security. This transaction did not reduce any other component of the money supply (not currency or traveler's checks). Therefore, the overall money supply has increased.

An open market purchase increases the money supply.

Open Market Sales

Suppose the Fed offers to sell you a government security for $10,000. You agree to buy the security. You give the Fed a check for $10,000, and the Fed gives you the government security.

Once the $10,000 check is given to the Fed, it is removed from the economy altogether. It is as if it disappears from the face of the earth. The total dollar amount of checking account deposits is $10,000 less than before the Fed sold you the government security.

An open market sale reduces the money supply.

Changing the Discount Rate

Suppose bank A wants to borrow $1 million. It could borrow the money from another bank (say, bank B), or it could borrow the money from the Fed. If bank A borrows the money from bank B, bank B will charge an interest rate. The interest rate charged by bank B is the **federal funds rate.** If bank A borrows the $1 million from the Fed, the Fed will charge an interest rate. The interest rate charged by the Fed is the **discount rate.**

If the federal funds rate is lower than the discount rate, bank A will borrow from bank B. However, if the discount rate is lower than the federal funds rate, bank A will probably borrow from the Fed.

If bank A borrows from bank B, no new money enters the economy. Bank B simply has $1 million less, and bank A has $1 million more. The total money supply hasn't changed.

If bank A borrows from the Fed, the Fed creates new money. The Fed creates the loan by creating funds out of thin air and depositing them into bank A's reserve account. The bank now has $1 million more reserves. The total money supply has increased. If the Fed lowers its discount rate so that it's lower than the federal funds rate, banks are likely to borrow from the Fed. When banks borrow from the Fed, the money supply increases.

If the Fed raises its discount rate so that it is higher than the federal funds rate, banks will begin to borrow from each other rather than from the Fed.

At some point, banks must repay the funds they borrow from the Fed. When the banks repay these loans, money is removed from the economy and the money supply drops. So, if the Fed raises its discount rate relative to the federal funds rate, the money supply will eventually fall.

The Federal Funds Target Rate

The Fed can change the money supply by setting the **federal funds rate target**. The federal funds rate target is the rate the Fed would like the federal funds rate to be.

The Discretion of the Fed

The Fed has the power today to increase and decrease the money supply of the country by any amount. Some economists argue that this kind of power can be abused and that it would be better if the Fed had to abide by some monetary rule. They argue that a monetary rule would help to create stability in the economy.

Gold Standard

Many people would like the United States to use a gold standard as a monetary rule. A gold standard would require the government to determine the price for gold and vow to buy and sell gold at that set price. As the market price of gold goes up and down, so do the prices of other goods and services, but the gold standard would stabilize the value of the dollar in terms of what a dollar can purchase.

Answer questions 1–3 in the Section 5 Assessment on page 311 of your textbook.

Name: _____ Date: _____

CHAPTER 10

Graphic Organizer Activity

Supply the missing words in the blank spaces of these graphic organizers.

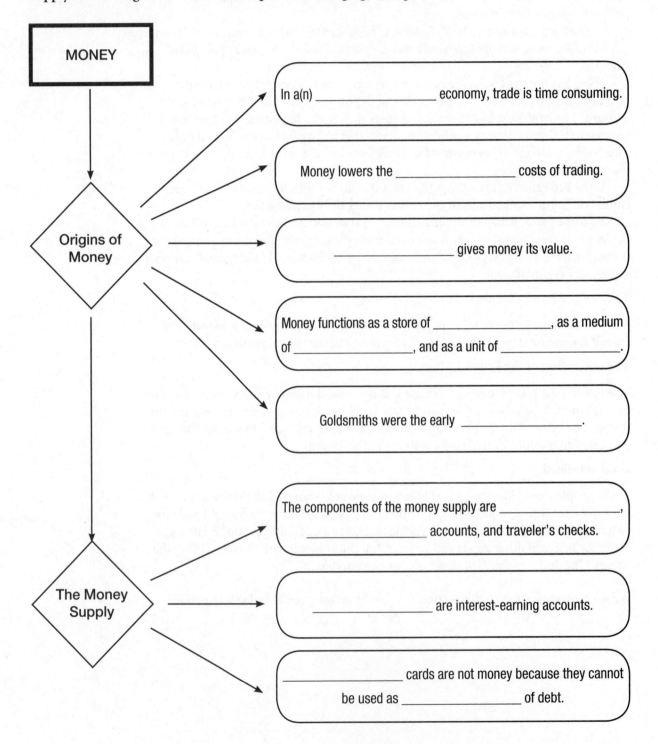

MONEY

Origins of Money

In a(n) _____ economy, trade is time consuming.

Money lowers the _____ costs of trading.

_____ gives money its value.

Money functions as a store of _____, as a medium of _____, and as a unit of _____.

Goldsmiths were the early _____.

The Money Supply

The components of the money supply are _____, _____ accounts, and traveler's checks.

_____ are interest-earning accounts.

_____ cards are not money because they cannot be used as _____ of debt.

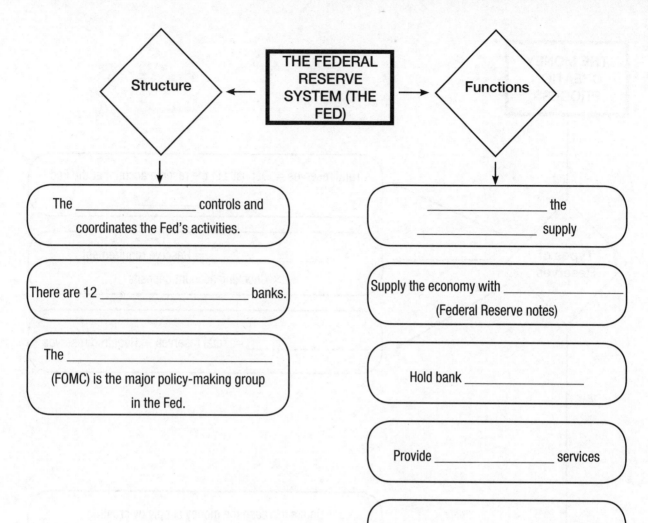

Structure

THE FEDERAL RESERVE SYSTEM (THE FED)

Functions

The _____ controls and coordinates the Fed's activities.

There are 12 _____ banks.

The _____ (FOMC) is the major policy-making group in the Fed.

_____ the _____ supply

Supply the economy with _____ (Federal Reserve notes)

Hold bank _____

Provide _____ services

_____ member banks

Serve as _____ of last resort

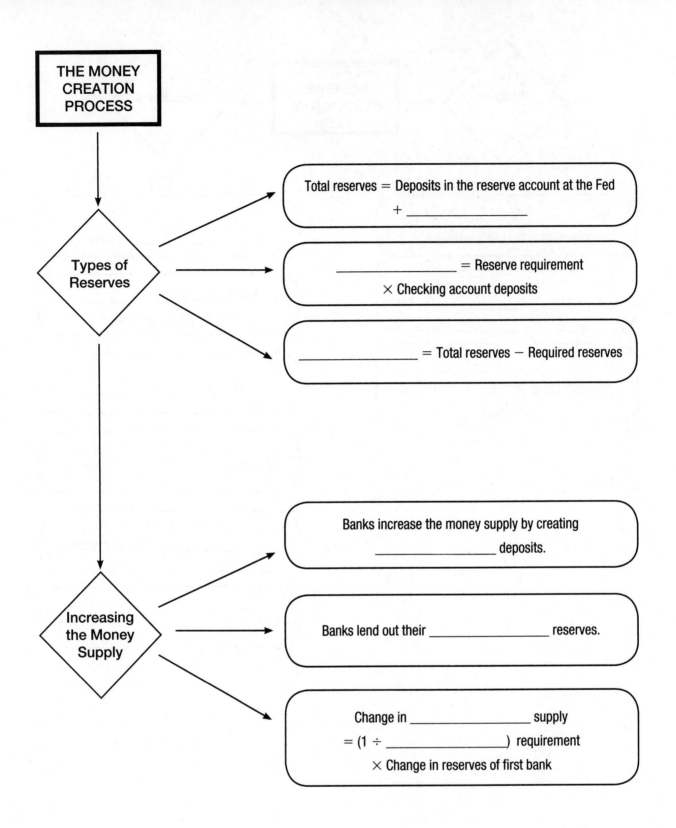

THE MONEY
CREATION
PROCESS

Types of
Reserves

Total reserves = Deposits in the reserve account at the Fed
+ _____

_____ = Reserve requirement
× Checking account deposits

_____ = Total reserves − Required reserves

Increasing
the Money
Supply

Banks increase the money supply by creating
_____ deposits.

Banks lend out their _____ reserves.

Change in _____ supply
= (1 ÷ _____) requirement
× Change in reserves of first bank

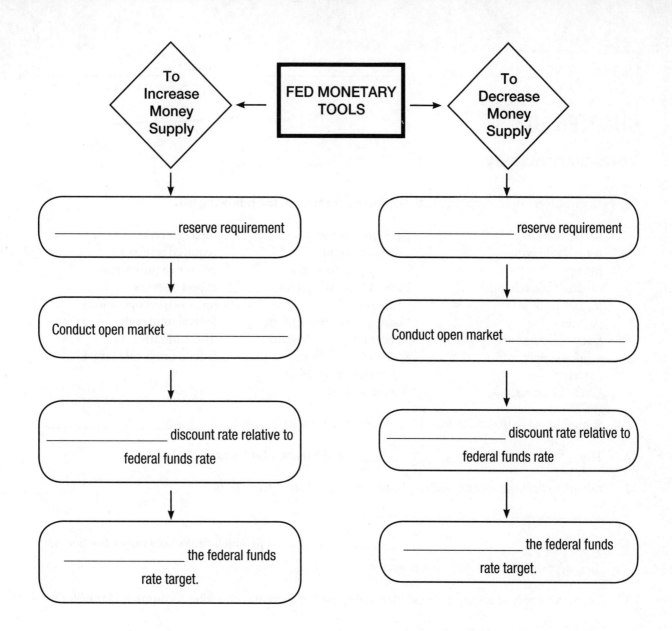

FED MONETARY TOOLS

To Increase Money Supply

_____ reserve requirement

Conduct open market _____

_____ discount rate relative to federal funds rate

_____ the federal funds rate target.

To Decrease Money Supply

_____ reserve requirement

Conduct open market _____

_____ discount rate relative to federal funds rate

_____ the federal funds rate target.

CHAPTER 10

Vocabulary Activity

For each question, fill in the blank with the correct term from the following list.

barter economy	demand deposit	total reserves
transaction costs	savings account	required reserves
money	loanable funds market	reserve requirement
medium of exchange	Federal Reserve System	excess reserves
unit of account	(the Fed)	open market operations
store of value	Board of Governors of the	federal funds rate
fractional reserve banking	Federal Reserve System	discount rate
money supply	Federal Open Market	federal funds rate target
currency	Committee (FOMC)	
Federal Reserve note	reserve account	

1. Something with the ability to hold value over time is a(n) _____.

2. The _____ is the market for loans.

3. A bank's checking account with its Federal Reserve district bank is its

   _____.

4. _____ is an arrangement in which banks hold only a fraction of

   their deposits and lend out the remainder.

5. The total supply of money in circulation, composed of currency, checking accounts, and traveler's

   checks, is the _____.

6. _____ are the costs associated with the time and effort needed to

   search out, negotiate, and consummate an exchange.

7. A good that is widely accepted for purposes of exchange and in the repayment of debt is

   _____.

8. _____ are the minimum amount of reserves a bank must hold

   against deposits as mandated by the Fed.

9. The buying and selling of government securities by the Fed is

   _____.

10. The central bank of the United States is the _____.

11. Anything that is generally acceptable in exchange for goods and services is a(n)

    _____.

12. The 12-member policy-making group within the Fed is the

_____.

13. A(n) _____ is a common measurement used to express values.

14. _____ are the sum of a bank's deposits in its reserve account at the Fed and its vault cash.

15. An economy in which trades are made in goods and services instead of in money is a(n)

_____.

16. An account from which deposited funds can be withdrawn in currency or transferred by a check to a third party at the initiative of the owner is a(n) _____.

17. The regulation that requires a bank to keep a certain percentage of its deposits in its reserve account with the Fed or in its vault as vault cash is the _____.

18. A(n) _____ is an interest-earning account.

19. _____ includes coins issued by the U.S. Treasury and paper money issued by the Federal Reserve System.

20. The interest rate one bank charges another for a loan is the _____.

21. Paper money issued by the Federal Reserve System is a(n) _____.

22. The rate that the Fed would like the federal funds rate to be is called the

_____.

23. The _____ is the governing body of the Federal Reserve System.

24. _____ are any reserves held beyond the required amount.

25. The interest rate the Fed charges a bank for a loan is the _____.

CHAPTER 10
Working with Graphs and Tables Activity

Fred magically creates $20,000 out of thin air. He opens a checking account at bank A and deposits the $20,000. Bank A lends out its excess reserves to Ned. Ned opens a checking account at bank B and deposits the amount of his loan. Bank B lends out its excess reserves to Ted. The process continues in the same way with banks C, D, E, and so on. The Fed has set the reserve requirement at 20 percent. Fill in the missing amounts in the following table.

Bank	New checking account deposits (new reserves)	Required reserves	Excess reserves, new loans, or new bank-created checking account deposits
A	$20,000	$4,000	
B			
C		$2,560	$10,240
D	$10,240		
E	$8,192	$1,638.40	$6,553.60
⋮	⋮	⋮	⋮
Totals	$100,000		

Created by Fred: _____

Created by banking system: + _____

Created by Fred and banking system: _____

CHAPTER 10
Practice Test

Matching

Each event describes a function of money. Write the letter of the correct function in the blank.

1. _____ Javier earns $200 and decides to save it for a future purchase.

2. _____ You notice that a new DVD costs $15.

3. _____ You pay $30 in cash for a new shirt.

4. _____ Your friend pays you $100 for your skateboard.

5. _____ You write a check for some new clothes.

6. _____ You put some loose change in your desk drawer.

7. _____ A salad costs $3 and a bowl of soup costs $2. You decide to have a salad for lunch.

a. medium of exchange
b. unit of account
c. store of value

Multiple Choice

Circle the letter of the correct answer.

1. What are coins issued by the U.S. Treasury and paper money issued by the Federal Reserve System called?

    a. currency
    b. demand deposits
    c. money supply
    d. checks

2. Which of the following Fed actions will increase the money supply?

    a. lower the reserve requirement
    b. raise the reserve requirement
    c. conduct open market sale
    d. raise the discount rate relative to the federal funds rate

3. Which of the following is an economy in which people trade goods and services for other goods and services?

    a. money economy
    b. reserve economy
    c. fractional economy
    d. barter economy

4. What do total reserves equal?

    a. checking account deposits plus vault cash plus credit cards
    b. bank deposits at the Fed plus vault cash
    c. vault cash plus currency outside of the bank
    d. bank deposits at the Fed

5. Which of the following is a good that is widely accepted for purposes of exchange and in the repayment of debt?

    a. money
    b. credit
    c. currency
    d. savings

6. Which of the following is a banking system in which banks hold only a fraction of their deposits and lend out the remainder?

    a. credit system
    b. lending system
    c. excess reserve system
    d. fractional reserve system

7. The total money supply is $100; $50 is in currency and $20 is in traveler's checks. Which of the following is true?

    a. $30 is in checking accounts.
    b. $30 is in savings accounts.
    c. $30 is in credit card purchases.
    d. $30 is near-money.

8. Which of the following is *not* a responsibility of the Fed?

    a. supplying paper money
    b. changing government spending
    c. providing check-clearing services
    d. supervising member banks

9. Which of the following Fed actions will decrease the money supply?

    a. an open market purchase of government securities
    b. an increase in the reserve requirement
    c. a decrease in the discount rate
    d. a decrease in the reserve requirement

10. Which of the following is the minimum amount of reserves a bank must hold against its deposits?
    a. excess reserves
    b. total reserves
    c. required reserves
    d. vault reserves

Short Answer

Write your answers on the lines provided.

1. How does money increase specialization?

    _____

    _____

    _____

    _____

2. What monetary tools are available to the Fed for changing the money supply? How does a change in each affect the money supply?

    _____

    _____

    _____

    _____

    _____

3. Credit cards can be used to buy goods and services. Then why aren't credit cards considered money?

    _____

    _____

    _____

CHAPTER 11, SECTION 1

Outlining Activity

Look through the chapter for an overview of the material. Pay attention to the main topics in the book. As you scan each section of the book, fill in the missing words in the following outline.

I. What Is Gross Domestic Product?

A. Gross domestic product (GDP) is the total market value of all _____ goods and services produced _____ in a country.

B. To calculate GDP, first find the _____ for each final good produced. (Multiply the price of each good by the quantity of the good produced.) Then, sum the market values.

II. Why Count Only Final Goods?

A. A final good is a good sold to its _____ user.

B. A(n) _____ good has not reached its _____ user.

C. In computing GDP, economists count only final goods to avoid _____, which is counting a good more than once.

III. Does GDP Omit Anything?

A. GDP omits _____ goods and services.

B. GDP omits _____ of legal goods and services with no records.

C. GDP omits some _____ goods and services.

D. GDP omits sales of _____ goods.

E. GDP omits _____ transactions and other _____ transactions.

F. GDP omits government _____ payments.

IV. The Difference Between GDP and GNP

A. Gross national product (GNP) is the total market value of final goods and services produced by U.S. citizens, no matter where in the world they reside.

B. GDP is the total market value of final goods and services produced within the _____ of the United States, no matter who produces them.

CHAPTER 11, SECTION 1

Just the Facts Handout

What Is Gross Domestic Product?

Gross domestic product (GDP) is the total market value of all final goods and services produced in a country in one year. To calculate GDP, complete the following steps:

1. Find the market value for each good produced: Multiply the price of each good by the quantity of the good produced.

2. Sum the market values: Add the dollar amounts found in step 1.

Example

A tiny economy has two goods, A and B. It produced 100 units of A and 200 units of B this year. The price of A is $4 and the price of B is $6. Find the market value for each good produced. The market value of good A = $4 × 100 units = $400. The market value of good B = $6 × 200 units = $1,200. Sum the market values. GDP = $400 + $1,200 = $1,600.

Why Count Only Final Goods?

GDP is the total market value of all *final* goods and services produced in a country in one year. A final good is a good sold to its final user. For example, when you buy a hamburger at a fast-food restaurant, the hamburger is a final good. You are the final user. No one uses (eats) the hamburger besides you. An intermediate good, in contrast, has not reached its final user.

When computing GDP, economists count only final goods and services. If they counted both final and intermediate goods and services, they would be **double counting**, or counting a good more than once.

Does GDP Omit Anything?

Some exchanges that take place in an economy are not included in the GDP measurement.

Illegal Goods and Services

For something to be included as part of GDP, we have to be able to count it. We cannot count illegal trades. No record is made of these transactions.

Transactions of Legal Goods and Services with No Record

Suppose a gardener mows someone's lawn and prunes the shrubbery for $35 a week. The gardener asks to be paid in cash and does not want a sales receipt for the work. No evidence shows that a transaction was ever made.

Some Nonmarket Goods and Services

Some goods and services are traded outside of official markets. Suppose Eileen Montoya cooks, cleans, and takes care of all financial matters in the Montoya household. She is not paid for doing these activities. She does not receive a weekly salary from the family. Because she is not paid, the value of her work is not counted in GDP.

Sales of Used Goods

The sale of a used good is not recorded in this year's GDP statistics. The value of a used good was counted when the good was originally produced. A used car is an example of such a good.

Stock Transactions and Other Financial Transactions

A stock transaction is not included in GDP because it is not a good or service. GDP counts only goods and services. A person who buys stock is not buying a good or a service. The person is buying a right to own part of the firm that originally issued the stock.

Government Transfer Payments

When the government makes a payment to someone, it often does not get a good or service in exchange. This type of payment is referred to as a government transfer payment. For example, a social security check is a government transfer payment.

GDP counts only current goods and services produced. A transfer payment has nothing to do with current goods and services produced. So, transfer payments are omitted from GDP statistics.

The Difference Between GDP and GNP

Gross national product (GNP) is the total market value of final goods and services produced by U.S. citizens, no matter where in the world they reside. GDP, in contrast, is the total market value of final goods and services produced within the borders of the United States, no matter who produces them. (See Exhibit 11-4 on page 320 of your textbook.)

Answer questions 1–4 in the Section 1 Assessment on page 320 of your textbook.

Guided Reading and Study Guide

CHAPTER 11, SECTION 2
Outlining Activity

Look through the chapter for an overview of the material. Pay attention to the main topics in the book. As you scan each section of the book, fill in the missing words in the following outline.

I. How Is GDP Measured?

A. Economists break the economy into four sectors: the _____ sector, the _____ sector, the _____ sector, and the _____ sector.

B. Economists give names to the expenditures made by each of the four sectors.

1. Expenditures made by the household sector (or by consumers) are called _____.

2. Expenditures made by the business sector are called _____.

3. Expenditures made by the government sector are called _____.

4. Expenditures made by the residents of other countries for U.S.-produced goods are called _____.

C. Economists also adjust for U.S. purchases of foreign-produced goods. Expenditures made by Americans for foreign-produced goods are called _____.

D. GDP equals the sum of _____ (C), _____ (I), _____ (G), and _____ (EX) minus _____ (IM).

II. Is Every Good That Is Produced Also Sold?

A. The definition of GDP refers to goods and services *produced*. The calculation of GDP refers to *expenditures* on goods and services. But not every good that is produced in a given year is sold.

B. Goods that are produced but not sold are included in GDP.

C. Statisticians assume that everything that is produced is purchased by someone. If a company doesn't sell a good it produced, statisticians assume the good is "purchased" by the company that produced it.

III. GDP Versus Quality of Life

A. Higher GDP does not necessarily mean greater _____.

B. There are many things, such as leisure time, that go into being better off or possessing greater well-being. Greater production of goods and services is only one of those things.

C. Higher GDP also does not necessarily mean higher _____ GDP. One country may have a higher GDP than another country, but on a per-person basis, each person could have fewer goods and services (on average) in the first country than in the second country.

Guided Reading and Study Guide

CHAPTER 11, SECTION 2

Just the Facts Handout

How Is GDP Measured?

Economists break the economy into four sectors: household, business, government, and foreign. The people in each of these sectors buy goods and services.

Economists give names to the expenditures made by each of the four sectors. The expenditures made by the household sector (or by consumers) are called **consumption**. The expenditures made by the business sector are called **investment**. The expenditures made by the government sector are called **government purchases**. (Government purchases include purchases made by all three levels of government—local, state, and federal.) The expenditures made by the residents of other countries on goods produced in the United States are called **export spending**.

All goods produced in the United States must be bought by the four sectors. However, people in the four sectors also purchase foreign-produced goods. To compute GDP, economists have to adjust for U.S. purchases of foreign-produced goods. Spending by Americans for foreign-produced goods is called **import spending**.

To compute U.S. GDP, we add consumption (C), investment (I), government purchases (G), and export spending (EX), and then subtract import spending (IM). In symbol form:

$$GDP = C + I + G + EX - IM$$

Is Every Good That Is Produced Also Sold?

The definition of GDP refers to goods and services *produced*. The calculation of GDP refers to *expenditures* on goods and services. Nevertheless, something that is produced but not purchased is included in GDP.

For example, suppose a car company produces 10,000 new cars this year. The household sector buys only 8,900 of the 10,000 cars. That means that 1,100 cars were produced but not sold. The government statisticians who compute GDP assume that everything that is produced is purchased by someone. They assume the 1,100 cars are "purchased" by the car company that produced them. These cars get counted in GDP.

GDP Versus Quality of Life

Quality of life is determined by a number of factors. A high GDP is only one of them. Look at the issue on an individual basis. One person may have many more expensive goods than another person has. However, the second person may have more time to enjoy life. We cannot say who is better off.

Similarly, country X may have a higher GDP than country Y. We cannot say that people in country X are better off. Being better off involves much more than simply how much output is produced.

When comparing countries, we need to look at more than their GDPs. We need to look at each country's per capita GDP—that is, its GDP divided by its population.

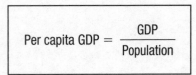

$$\text{Per capita GDP} = \frac{\text{GDP}}{\text{Population}}$$

This gives us the average amount of goods and services each person in the country has. Suppose country X has double the GDP of country Y. However, the population of country X is three times the population of country Y. On average, each person in country X has fewer goods and services than does each person in country Y. In short, higher GDP does not necessarily mean higher per capita GDP.

Answer questions 1–4 in the Section 2 Assessment on page 326 of your textbook.

CHAPTER 11, SECTION 3

Outlining Activity

Look through the chapter for an overview of the material. Pay attention to the main topics in the book. As you scan each section of the book, fill in the missing words in the following outline.

   I. The Two Variables of GDP: P and Q

     A. If GDP increased from one year to the next, you can't tell whether GDP increased because

        _____ increased, because _____ increased, or

        because both increased.

     B. Economists keep _____ constant to find out what causes a rise in GDP.

     C. Economists use the prices that existed in one particular year in the past, called the

        _____, and compute _____.

     D. GDP is measured using price in the _____ year multiplied by quantity in

        the current year.

     E. Real GDP is measured using price in the _____ year multiplied by

        quantity in the current year.

     F. Economists prefer working with real GDP to working with GDP because they know that if

        real GDP in one year is higher than real GDP in another year, _____ is

        greater in the year with the higher real GDP.

CHAPTER 11, SECTION 3

Just the Facts Handout

The Two Variables of GDP: P and Q

To compute GDP in a simple, one-good economy, we multiplied price (P) by quantity (Q) to find GDP. If either P or Q rises and the other remains constant, GDP will rise.

To see how this relationship works, look at the following table:

Price	Quantity	GDP
$10	2	$20
$15	2	$30
$10	3	$30

With a price of $10 and a quantity of 2, GDP is $20. When the price rises to $15 and the quantity stays at 2, GDP rises to $30. When the price stays at $10 and the quantity rises to 3, GDP again is $30. GDP can increase because price increases, because quantity of output increases, or because both price and quantity increase.

To find out whether an increase in price, quantity, or both causes a rise in GDP, economists keep price constant. If price stays constant, then any rise in GDP must be due to a rise in quantity.

Economists keep price constant by using the price that existed in one particular year in the past. This year is called the **base year**.

GDP that is measured in base-year prices is **real GDP**. When real GDP is computed, the outputs of different years are priced at base-year levels. Recall that GDP is measured using price in the current year multiplied by quantity in the current year. In contrast, real GDP is measured using price in the base year multiplied by quantity in the current year. (See Exhibit 11-7 on page 328 of your textbook.)

Economists prefer working with real GDP to working with GDP. They know that if real GDP in one year is higher than real GDP in another year, output is greater in the year with the higher real GDP.

Answer questions 1–4 in the Section 3 Assessment on page 330 of your textbook.

CHAPTER 11, SECTION 4

Outlining Activity

Look through the chapter for an overview of the material. Pay attention to the main topics in the book. As you scan each section of the book, fill in the missing words in the following outline.

I. Calculating the Change in a Single Price

A. You can use a formula to find what percentage the price of a good increased or decreased between two years—the _____ change in price.

$$\text{Percentage change in price} = \frac{\text{Price in later year} - \text{Price in earlier year}}{\text{Price in earlier year}} \times 100$$

II. The Consumer Price Index

A. A(n) _____ is a measure of the price level, or the average level of prices.

B. The most widely cited price index is the _____ (CPI).

C. The U.S. Bureau of Labor Statistics calculates the CPI.

D. The bureau samples thousands of households and determines what these consumers paid for a representative group of goods called the _____. This is compared with what a typical "consumer unit" paid for the same _____ in 1982–1984.

E. Calculating the CPI involves two steps.

   1. Calculate the total _____ on the market basket in the _____ year and the total _____ on the market basket in the _____ year.

   2. Divide the total current-year expenditure by the total base-year expenditure and multiply by 100.

$$\text{CPI}_{\text{current year}} = \frac{\text{Total current-year expenditure}}{\text{Total base-year expenditure}} \times 100$$

F. Two CPI numbers can be used to figure out the _____ by which prices increased between two years.

$$\text{Percentage change in CPI} = \frac{\text{CPI}_{\text{later year}} - \text{CPI}_{\text{earlier year}}}{\text{CPI}_{\text{earlier year}}} \times 100$$

III. Determining the Quantity of Goods and Services and the Price Level

A. A(n) _____ (AD) curve shows the quantity of goods and services buyers are willing and able to buy at different price _____ .

    1. An AD curve is _____ sloping. People are willing and able to buy _____ at _____ price levels than at higher price levels.

B. A(n) _____ (AS) curve shows the quantity of goods and services, or output, that producers are willing and able to supply at different price levels.

    1. An AS curve is _____ sloping. Sellers are willing and able to produce and sell _____ at _____ price levels than at lower price levels.

C. The _____ price level and the _____ quantity of goods and services are determined by the forces of aggregate demand and aggregate supply.

    1. At price levels _____ equilibrium price, there is a _____ of goods and services. As a result, the price level _____, people buy _____ goods and services, and producers produce _____. The surplus begins to disappear.

    2. At price levels _____ equilibrium price, there is a _____ of goods and services. As a result, the price level _____, people buy _____ goods and services, and producers produce _____. The shortage begins to disappear.

D. One of the factors that aggregate demand and aggregate supply affect is _____ .

IV. Who Are the Unemployed?

A. The total population can be divided into two broad groups.

    1. One group consists of persons under sixteen years of age, persons in the armed forces, and persons in mental or correctional facilities.

2. A second group consists of all others in the total population, or the

_____.

B. The noninstitutional adult civilian population is divided into two groups: persons not in the labor force and persons in the civilian labor force.

C. The persons not in the labor force are those who are neither working nor looking for work.

D. Persons in the civilian labor force can be divided into two groups. They are either

_____ or _____.

> Civilian labor force = Unemployed persons + Employed persons

V. The Unemployment and Employment Rates

A. The unemployment rate is the percentage of the _____ that is unemployed.

B. The unemployment rate is equal to the number of unemployed persons divided by the _____ labor force.

$$\text{Unemployment rate} = \frac{\text{Unemployed persons}}{\text{Civilian labor force}}$$

C. The employment rate is the percentage of the _____ that is employed.

D. The employment rate is equal to the number of persons _____ divided by the number of persons in the noninstitutional adult civilian population.

$$\text{Employment rate} = \frac{\text{Employed persons}}{\text{Noninstitutional adult civilian population}}$$

CHAPTER 11, SECTION 4

Just the Facts Handout

Calculating the Change in a Single Price

Suppose a Honda Accord was priced at $20,000 in 2014 and at $21,500 in 2015. Use the following formula to determine the percentage change in price:

$$\text{Percentage change in price for the Honda Accord} = \frac{\$21,500 - \$20,000}{\$20,000} \times 100$$

$$= \frac{\$1,500}{\$20,000} \times 100$$

$$= 0.075 \times 100$$

$$= 7.5\%$$

The Consumer Price Index

Economists are interested in what happens to prices in general rather than what happens to a single price. To observe what happens to prices, they need to calculate how prices change from one year to the next. Before they can do this, they need to compute a **price index**, or average price level. The most widely used price index is the **consumer price index (CPI)**.

The CPI is calculated by the U.S. Bureau of Labor Statistics. The bureau asks thousands of households what they paid for certain goods that represent all other purchases. This group of goods is called the market basket. Calculating the CPI involves two steps: (See Exhibit 11-8 on page 332 of your textbook.)

1. Calculate the total dollar expenditure on the market basket in the base year. Also calculate the total dollar expenditure on the market basket in the current year.
2. Divide the total expenditure in the current year by the total expenditure in the base year, and multiply by 100.

We can use two CPI numbers to figure out the percentage increase in prices between two years. We calculate this percentage increase in the same way that we determined the percentage increase for a single price. For example, in the United States in 2015, the CPI was 236.5. In 2016, the CPI was 241.4. Using the following formula, we find the percentage increase:

$$\text{Percentage change in U.S. CPI between 2015 and 2016} = \frac{241.4 - 236.5}{236.5} \times 100$$

$$= \frac{4.9}{236.5} \times 100$$

$$= 0.0207 \times 100$$

$$= 2.07\%$$

Determining the Quantity of Goods and Services and the Price Level

An economy has a demand side and a supply side. The demand side is represented by the aggregate demand curve. The **aggregate demand curve** shows the quantity of goods and services that buyers are willing and able to buy at different price levels. The supply side is represented by the aggregate supply curve. The **aggregate supply curve** shows the quantity of goods and services, or output, that producers are willing and able to supply at different price levels.

The forces of aggregate demand and aggregate supply determine the equilibrium price level. They also determine the equilibrium quantity of goods and services. (See Exhibit 11-9 on page 334 of your textbook.) The equilibrium price level and the equilibrium quantity of goods and services, or output, come to exist over time.

At price levels above the equilibrium price, there is a surplus of goods and services. As a result, the price level drops. At a lower price level, people buy more goods and services. Also, producers produce less. The surplus begins to disappear because of these actions. (Buyers are helping to eliminate the surplus by buying more. Sellers are helping to eliminate the surplus by producing less.)

At price levels below the equilibrium price, there is a shortage of goods and services. The price level rises. People buy fewer goods and services. Also, producers produce more. The shortage begins to disappear because of these actions. (Buyers are helping to eliminate the shortage by buying less. Sellers are helping to eliminate the shortage by producing more.)

Aggregate demand and supply are influenced by a number of factors. They also influence other factors. One of the factors that aggregate demand and supply influence is unemployment.

Who Are the Unemployed?

The total population can be divided into two broad groups. One group includes persons under sixteen years of age, persons in the armed forces, and persons in mental or correctional facilities. The other group includes all other people. This group is called the noninstitutional adult civilian population.

The noninstitutional adult civilian population is also divided into two groups. One group is persons not in the labor force. This includes people who are not working and are not looking for work. The other group is persons in the labor force.

Persons in the labor force can also be divided into two groups. One group is persons who are employed. The other group is persons who are not employed. (See Exhibit 11-10 on page 337 of your textbook.)

The Unemployment and Employment Rates

The **unemployment rate** is the percentage of the civilian labor force that is unemployed. It is equal to the number of unemployed persons divided by the civilian labor force.

For example, suppose the civilian labor force totals 10 million and the number of persons unemployed is 1 million. Then the unemployment rate is 10 percent.

The **employment rate** is the percentage of the noninstitutional adult civilian population that is employed. It is equal to the number of persons employed divided by the number of persons in the noninstitutional adult civilian population.

Answer questions 1–3 in the Section 4 Assessment on page 337 of your textbook.

CHAPTER 11

Graphic Organizer Activity

Supply the missing words in the blank spaces of these graphic organizers.

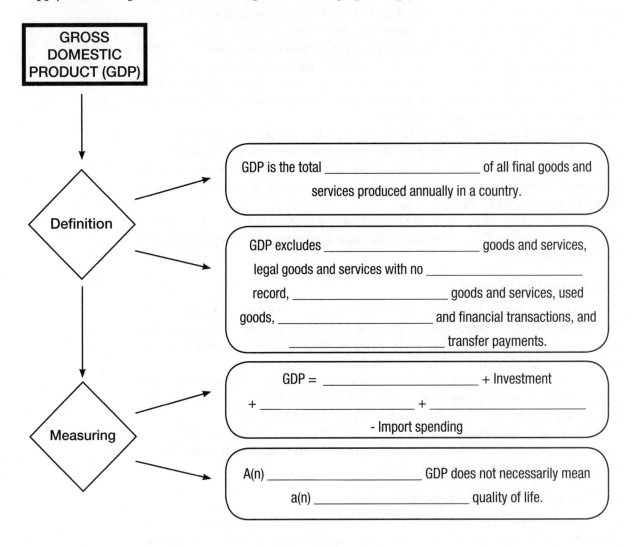

GROSS DOMESTIC PRODUCT (GDP)

Definition

GDP is the total _____ of all final goods and services produced annually in a country.

GDP excludes _____ goods and services, legal goods and services with no _____ record, _____ goods and services, used goods, _____ and financial transactions, and _____ transfer payments.

Measuring

GDP = _____ + Investment + _____ + _____ - Import spending

A(n) _____ GDP does not necessarily mean a(n) _____ quality of life.

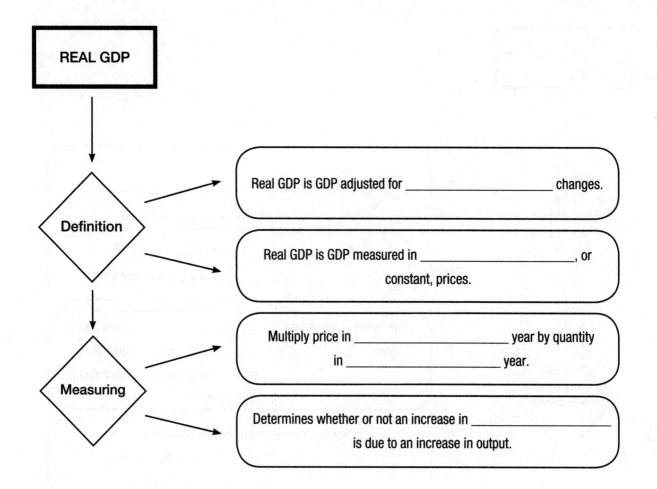

REAL GDP

Definition

Real GDP is GDP adjusted for _____ changes.

Real GDP is GDP measured in _____, or constant, prices.

Measuring

Multiply price in _____ year by quantity in _____ year.

Determines whether or not an increase in _____ is due to an increase in output.

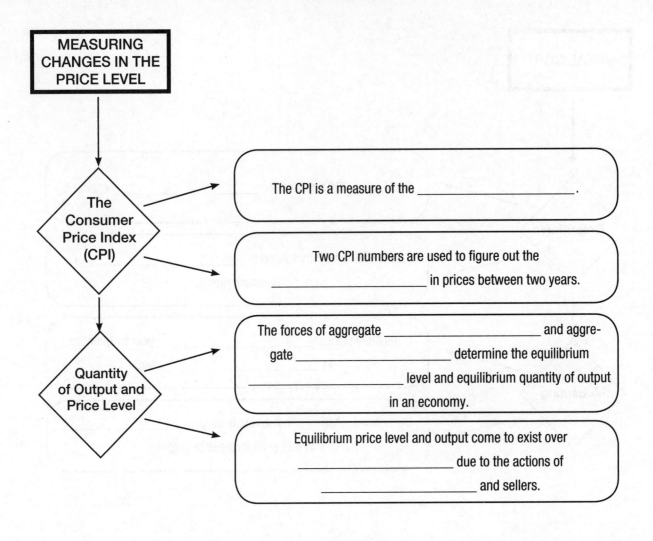

MEASURING
CHANGES IN THE
PRICE LEVEL

The
Consumer
Price Index
(CPI)

The CPI is a measure of the _____.

Two CPI numbers are used to figure out the
_____ in prices between two years.

Quantity
of Output and
Price Level

The forces of aggregate _____ and aggregate _____ determine the equilibrium _____ level and equilibrium quantity of output in an economy.

Equilibrium price level and output come to exist over _____ due to the actions of _____ and sellers.

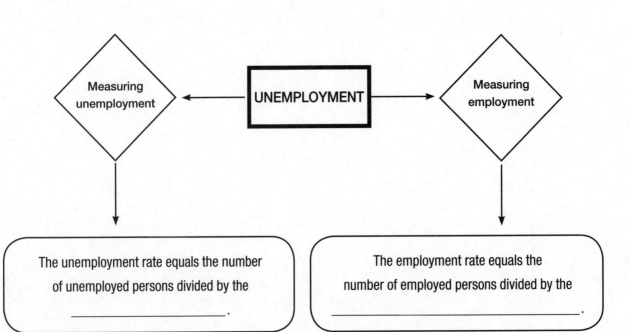

Measuring
unemployment

UNEMPLOYMENT

Measuring
employment

The unemployment rate equals the number of unemployed persons divided by the _____.

The employment rate equals the number of employed persons divided by the _____.

CHAPTER 11

Vocabulary Activity

For each question, fill in the blank with the correct term from the following list.

gross domestic product (GDP)   export spending   consumer price index (CPI)
double counting   import spending   aggregate demand curve
consumption   base year   aggregate supply curve
investment   real GDP   unemployment rate
government purchases   price index   employment rate

1. A benchmark year—a year chosen as a point of reference for comparison—is a(n) _____.

2. The total market value of all final goods and services produced annually in a country is _____ (GDP).

3. _____ is the amount spent by the residents of other countries for goods produced in the United States.

4. The _____ is the percentage of the civilian labor force that is unemployed.

5. Counting a good more than once in computing GDP is _____.

6. Expenditures made by the business sector are _____.

7. The _____ shows the quantity of goods and services that buyers are willing and able to buy at different price levels.

8. A measure of the price level, or the average level of prices, is a(n) _____.

9. The _____ is the percentage of the noninstitutional adult civilian population that is employed.

10. Expenditures made by the government sector are _____.

11. The _____ (CPI) is the most widely cited price index.

12. The _____ shows the quantity of goods and services that producers are willing and able to supply at different price levels.

13. _____ is gross domestic product that has been adjusted for price changes.

14. Expenditures made by the household sector are _____.

15. The amount spent by Americans on foreign-produced goods is _____.

Name: _____   Date: _____

CHAPTER 11

Working with Graphs and Tables Activity

Suppose you want to measure changes in the prices of goods and services. Assume the market basket of goods and services includes only three items—hats, gloves, and pens. The following table shows the prices and quantities produced of these goods for three years. Use the table to answer the questions that follow. Write your answers on the lines provided.

Year	Price of hats	Quantity of hats produced	Price of gloves	Quantity of gloves produced	Price of pens	Quantity of pens produced
2013	$10	20	$5	50	$1	55
2014	$12	20	$5	55	$2	60
2015	$12	30	$7	60	$3	70

1. The total dollar expenditure for year 2013 equals _____.

2. The total dollar expenditure for year 2014 equals _____.

3. The total dollar expenditure for year 2015 equals _____.

4. Let the year 2013 be the base year. Then, the CPI for year 2014 equals _____.
   The CPI for year 2015 equals _____.

5. The percentage change in the CPI from 2014 to 2015 equals _____.

CHAPTER 11

Practice Test

Multiple Choice

Circle the letter of the correct answer.

1. Suppose the CPI in 2015 was 85 and the CPI in 2014 was 100. Which of the following is true?

   a. The CPI increased 15 percent in 2015.
   b. The CPI decreased 15 percent in 2015.
   c. The CPI increased 17.6 percent in 2015.
   d. The CPI decreased 17.6 percent in 2015.

2. Which of the following would be included in the measurement of U.S. GDP?

   a. the value of the steel used to produce new cars
   b. the value of used textbooks sold to your school
   c. the value of illegal activities
   d. the value of new shoes produced in the United States

3. Why does the aggregate demand curve slope downward?

   a. At higher price levels, firms will offer more output to be sold.
   b. As the price level increases, it costs more to produce goods.
   c. People are willing and able to buy a greater quantity of goods and services at lower price levels.
   d. All of the above explain why the aggregate demand curve slopes downward.

4. If GDP increases from one year to the next, which of the following is true?

   a. Prices have increased.
   b. Quantity of output has increased.
   c. Both prices and quantity of output have increased.
   d. Any of the above could be true.

5. If GDP is higher in country A than it is in country B, which of the following is true?

   a. Per capita GDP is higher in country A.
   b. People in country A are better off than people in country B.
   c. Per capita GDP is higher in country B.
   d. Any of the above could be true.

6. Last year, a tiny economy produced 20 sofas, 30 chairs, and 50 bookcases. The price of a sofa is $1,500, the price of a chair is $400, and the price of a bookcase is $250. What was the GDP for this economy last year?

   a. $54,500
   b. $64,500
   c. $27,500
   d. $55,000

7. Which of the following are included in the civilian labor force?

   a. persons in the armed forces
   b. persons who are retired
   c. unemployed persons
   d. persons who are not looking for work

8. Suppose consumption in an economy is $600 billion; government purchases are $200 billion; export spending is $230 billion; import spending is $150 billion; and investment is $200 billion. What does GDP equal?

   a. $1,590 billion
   b. $1,080 billion
   c. $1,380 billion
   d. none of the above

9. If real GDP increases from one year to the next, which of the following is true?

   a. Prices have increased.
   b. Quantity of output has increased.
   c. Both prices and quantity of output have increased.
   d. Any of the above could be true.

10. Samantha, a U.S. citizen, owns a business in Canada. Where would the value of the output she is producing be counted?

    a. GNP
    b. GDP
    c. real GDP
    d. CPI

11. Which of the following do you need to compute the percentage change in the CPI between 2011 and 2014?

    a. the total dollar expenditure on the market basket in 2011
    b. the CPI in 2014
    c. the CPI in the base year
    d. real GDP

12. The noninstitutional adult civilian population is 130 million, 50 million persons are not in the labor force, and the number of employed persons is 75 million. What is the unemployment rate?

    a. 6.67 percent
    b. 10 percent
    c. 6.25 percent
    d. 3.75 percent

Short Answer

Write your answers on the lines provided.

1. Explain the difference between real GDP and GDP.

2. Describe the steps in computing the CPI.

3. Does a high GDP necessarily mean a country is better off? Explain your answer.

CHAPTER 12, SECTION 1

Outlining Activity

Look through the chapter for an overview of the material. Pay attention to the main topics in the book. As you scan each section of the book, fill in the missing words in the following outline.

I. What Is Inflation?

   A. Inflation is an increase in the _____ level (or _____

   level of _____).

II. How Do We Measure Inflation?

   A. The inflation rate between two years is the percentage change in the _____.

$$\text{Inflation Rate} = \frac{\text{CPI later year} - \text{CPI earlier year}}{\text{CPI earlier year}} \times 100$$

   B. A(n) _____ change (rise) in the _____ means
inflation occurred.

III. Demand-Side Versus Supply-Side Inflation

   A. If aggregate demand _____ and aggregate supply stays the same,

   _____ inflation will occur.

     1. A(n) _____ in aggregate demand shifts the AD curve to the

     _____. This _____ the price level, so we have

     inflation.

     2. A(n) _____ in the money supply is one of the things that can cause

     _____.

   B. If aggregate supply _____ and aggregate demand stays the same,

   _____ will occur.

     1. A(n) _____ in aggregate supply shifts the AS curve to the

     _____. This _____ the price level, so we

     have inflation.

     2. A major _____ that lowers agricultural output is one of the things that

     can _____ cause .

C. If aggregate demand _____ by more than aggregate supply

_____, the price level rises and we have inflation.

IV. The Simple Quantity Theory of Money

A. _____ is the average number of times a dollar is spent to buy final goods

and services.

    1. Velocity is calculated by finding the sum of the times each dollar changed hands and then

    dividing by the number of dollars.

B. The exchange equation is $M \times V = P \times Q$, where M is the _____

supply, P is the _____ level or average _____, Q is

_____ of _____, and V is _____.

C. The simple quantity theory of money uses the exchange equation to explain inflation.

    1. _____ (V) is assumed to be _____ in the simple

    quantity theory of money.

    2. The quantity of output, or goods and services, (Q) is also assumed to be constant.

    3. Then an increase in the money supply (M) causes an increase in the price level (P).

D. The simple quantity theory of money predicts that changes in the money supply will bring

about strictly proportional changes in the price level.

E. In the real world, the _____ changes predicted by the theory usually do not

happen. However, we usually find that the greater the _____ in the money

supply, the greater the _____ in the price level.

V. The Effects of Inflation

A. Inflation harms individuals on _____ incomes.

B. Inflation harms _____.

C. Inflation often turns past decisions into _____.

D. Inflation causes people to try to _____ against inflation (try to figure out

what investments offer the best protection against inflation).

    1. _____ requires an expenditure on resources. It diverts resources away

    from being used to produce goods.

VI. What Is Deflation?

A. Deflation is a(n) _____ in the price level, or the average level of prices.

B. Deflation is measured the same way inflation is measured.

C. A(n) _____ (downward) change in the CPI indicates deflation.

VII. Demand-Side Versus Supply-Side Deflation

A. If aggregate demand _____ and aggregate supply stays the same, _____ deflation will occur.

    1. A(n) _____ in aggregate demand shifts the AD curve to the _____. This _____ the price level, so we have deflation.

    2. A(n) _____ in the money supply is one of the things that can cause _____.

B. If aggregate supply _____ and aggregate demand stays the same, _____ deflation will occur.

    1. A(n) _____ in aggregate supply shifts the AS curve to the _____. This _____ the price level, so we have deflation.

    2. An increase in technology that makes it possible to produce more goods and services is one of the things that can cause _____.

VIII. Simple Quantity Theory of Money and Deflation

A. The simple quantity theory of money can be used to explain _____ .

B. A(n) _____ in the money supply will bring about deflation, assuming that velocity and the quantity of goods and services do not change.

IX. A Major Effect of Deflation

A. When all prices do not fall at the same time, deflation can lead to firms going out of business and workers being _____ .

CHAPTER 12, SECTION 1

Just the Facts Handout

What Is Inflation?

Every good in an economy has a price. An average of all these prices is the price level. **Inflation** is an increase in the price level, or an increase in the average level of prices.

How Do We Measure Inflation?

We know that inflation has occurred if the price level has increased. We measure the price level using the consumer price index (CPI). If the CPI has increased, the price level has increased and inflation has occurred.

For example, suppose the CPI was 180 last year. This year it is 187. The increase in the CPI means that inflation has occurred. We use the inflation rate to measure *how much* inflation has occurred. We find the inflation rate by using the same formula we used to find the percentage change in the CPI. (Recall that we used this formula in Chapter 11.)

$$\text{Inflation rate} = \frac{\text{CPI later year} - \text{CPI earlier year}}{\text{CPI earlier year}} \times 100$$

$$= \frac{187 - 180}{180} \times 100$$

$$= \frac{7}{180} \times 100$$

$$= 0.0389 \times 100$$

$$= 3.89\%$$

The positive change (rise) in the CPI shows that inflation occurred. The inflation rate is 3.89 percent.

Demand-Side Versus Supply-Side Inflation

The demand side of the economy is represented by aggregate demand. The supply side of the economy is represented by aggregate supply.

If aggregate demand increases and aggregate supply stays the same, the price level rises. (See Exhibit 12-3[a] on page 348 of your textbook.) A rise in the price level means inflation has occurred. This increase in the price level is caused by a change on the demand side of the economy. Economists call this type of inflation **demand-side inflation**. An increase in the money supply is one of the things that can cause demand-side inflation.

If aggregate supply decreases and aggregate demand stays the same, the price level rises. (See Exhibit 12-3[b] on page 348 of your textbook.) A rise in the price level means inflation has occurred. This increase in the price level is caused by a change on the supply side of the economy. Economists call this type of inflation **supply-side inflation**. A major drought can cause supply-side inflation by lowering the output of crops like corn.

The Simple Quantity Theory of Money

The simple quantity theory of money is used to explain inflation. The theory is based on the exchange equation.

The exchange equation is $M \times V = P \times Q$. In this equation, M stands for the money supply, V stands for velocity, P stands for the price level or average price, and Q stands for the quantity of output (quantity of goods and services). **Velocity** is the average number of times a dollar is spent to buy final goods and services. The exchange equation says that the money supply multiplied by velocity must equal the price level multiplied by the quantity of output. In other words, M multiplied by V must equal P times Q.

The **simple quantity theory of money** is used to explain inflation. It says that changes in the money supply will bring about strictly proportional changes in the price level. The theory makes two assumptions. It assumes that velocity (V) is constant and that quantity of output (Q) is constant. If V and Q don't change, then any change in P must be caused by a change in M. In addition, the change in P must be proportional to the change in M. This means that P must change by the same percentage as M changes.

For example, the theory predicts that if the money supply increases by 20 percent, the price level will increase by 20 percent. If the money supply increases by 100 percent, then the price level will increase by 100 percent.

In the real world, changes are not always strictly proportional. An increase in the money supply of, say, 10 percent does not usually bring about a 10 percent increase in the price level. However, we do usually see that the greater the increase in the money supply, the greater the increase in the price level. For example, a nation that increased its money supply by 30 percent would usually have a higher inflation rate than a nation that increased its money supply by 20 percent.

The Effects of Inflation

Many people are affected by inflation.

Inflation and Individuals on Fixed Incomes

Inflation lowers the purchasing power of money. After inflation occurs, a given amount of money will buy fewer units of goods. This means that if a person does not make more money, she or he will not be able to buy as much. Therefore, inflation lowers the standard of living for people on fixed incomes.

Inflation and Savers

Suppose the inflation rate is 10 percent and the interest rate is 6 percent. Then the increase from saving is less than the increase in prices. Saving makes a person worse off.

Inflation and Past Decisions

Inflation can turn past decisions into mistakes. Suppose that last year, a building contractor signed a contract to build a shopping mall for $30 million. The contractor estimated it would cost $28 million to buy the materials and hire the labor to build the mall. This year, because of inflation, the prices of labor and materials have increased. Now the contractor realizes it will cost $31 million to build the mall. The contractor looks at the decision to build the mall for only $30 million as a mistake—a costly mistake.

Inflation and Hedging Against Inflation

If inflation occurs often, people will try to **hedge** against it. They will try to figure out what they can invest in to protect themselves against it. They will use resources in their efforts to protect against inflation. Those resources will not be available for use in producing goods.

What Is Deflation?

Deflation is a decrease in the price level, or the average level of prices. We measure deflation the same way we measure inflation. We find the percentage change in the CPI between two years. If the change in the CPI is negative, we know that deflation has occurred.

Demand-Side Versus Supply-Side Deflation

Just like inflation, deflation can be due to a change on the demand side of the economy or to a change on the supply side of the economy.

If aggregate demand decreases and aggregate supply stays the same, the price level will fall and deflation will occur. (See Exhibit 12-6[a] on page 354 of your textbook.) A decrease in the money supply is one of the things that can cause demand-side deflation.

If aggregate supply increases and aggregate demand stays the same, the price level will fall and deflation will occur. (See Exhibit 12-6[b] on page 354 of your textbook.) Many things can cause supply-side deflation. One thing is an advance in technology that makes it possible to produce more goods and services with the same level of resources.

Simple Quantity Theory of Money and Deflation

The simple quantity theory of money can be used to explain deflation as well as inflation. The same assumptions hold: velocity and the quantity of goods and services do not change. The theory predicts that a fall in the money supply will bring about a strictly proportional fall in the price level.

A Major Effect of Deflation

Deflation can cause a problem for businesses because prices usually do not all fall at the same time.

For example, suppose Latoya produces wooden tables, and deflation occurs. The price of wooden tables falls first. The prices of wood, glue, and workers don't fall until many months later.

Because the price of wooden tables has fallen, Latoya's total revenue falls. However, the prices of wood, glue, and workers stay the same for a few months. So Latoya's total costs stay the same. As a result, Latoya's profit falls. Profit falls so much that Latoya ends up closing her shop, laying off her employees, and looking for different work.

Answer questions 1–5 in the Section 1 Assessment on page 357 of your textbook.

CHAPTER 12, SECTION 2

Outlining Activity

Look through the chapter for an overview of the material. Pay attention to the main topics in the book. As you scan each section of the book, fill in the missing words in the following outline.

I. What Is a Business Cycle?

A. _____ is calculated by multiplying the quantity of goods and services produced in a country in the current year times the prices that existed in a base year.

$$\text{Real GDP} = P_{\text{Base Year}} \times Q_{\text{Current Year}}$$

B. A business cycle is the _____ and _____ in economic activity, as measured by changes in _____.

C. Economists usually talk about four or five phases of the business cycle.

   1. At the _____ of a business cycle, real GDP is at a temporary high.

   2. A(n) _____ is a decrease in real GDP. A(n) _____ is a decline in real GDP for two consecutive quarters.

   3. A(n) _____ is the low point in real GDP, just before it begins to turn up.

   4. The _____ is the period when real GDP is rising. It begins at the trough and ends at the initial peak.

   5. A(n) _____ refers to increases in real GDP beyond the recovery.

D. An entire business cycle is measured from _____ to _____.

II. Forecasting Business Cycles

A. Economists have devised a few indicators of the _____ and sickness of the economy. These indicators _____ economic upturns or downturns (in real GDP), coincide with economic upturns or downturns, or lag behind economic upturns and downturns.

B. We expect a(n) _____ indicator to _____ before an

upturn in real GDP and _____ before a downturn in real GDP.

C. We expect a(n) _____ indicator to reach its _____ point

at the same time as a peak of a business cycle and to reach its _____ point

with the trough.

D. We expect a(n) _____ indicator to reach its _____

sometime after the peak of a business cycle and to reach its _____ sometime

after the trough.

E. A few of the leading indicators include _____ prices, the

_____ supply (in inflation-adjusted dollars), _____

expectations, and _____ hours worked in manufacturing.

III. What Causes the Business Cycle?

A. _____ Supply

1. When either the absolute money supply _____, or the growth rate in the

money supply _____, people end up buying fewer goods and services

and the economy falls into a contraction.

2. A(n) _____ in the money supply means more _____

and leads to an economic expansion.

3. Some economists say the erratic behavior of the monetary authorities or the Fed causes the

ups and downs of the business cycle.

B. Business Investment, Residential Construction, and Government Spending

1. A contraction might result from a cutback in business _____ or

government spending that lowers aggregate _____ in the economy.

Lower aggregate _____ means firms may _____

workers. _____ workers don't have the income they once had, so overall

income in the economy _____ . And with a lower income, people do not

buy as many goods.

2. Things are reversed when either the business sector or government starts to spend more.

C. Politics

    1. Some economists believe that some business cycles have been caused by

    _____ trying to get reelected to office.

    2. Politicians try to _____ government spending to increase aggregate

    _____ in the economy.

    3. With greater aggregate _____, firms will sell more goods and services

    and hire more workers.

    4. When times are good, voters are likely to reward the people in office who (they believe)

    made this possible.

    5. After the election, Congress may want to _____ spending to

    _____ aggregate demand and avoid _____.

    6. If Congress cuts spending too much, though, the economy could slide into a contraction.

D. Innovation

    1. Innovations can stimulate business cycles.

E. Supply Shocks

    1. _____ are major supply-side changes in the economy that reduce the

    capacity of the economy to produce.

    2. Firms end up producing less, so they fire some of their workers. Real GDP goes

    _____ and the unemployment rate goes _____.

CHAPTER 12, SECTION 2

Just the Facts Handout

What Is a Business Cycle?

Real GDP is GDP adjusted for price changes. To calculate real GDP, we multiply the quantity of goods and services produced in a country in the current year by the prices that existed in a base year.

A **business cycle** is the rising and falling of real GDP. A business cycle has the following five phases:
1. *Peak.* At the peak of a cycle, real GDP is at a temporary high.
2. *Contraction.* If real GDP decreases, the economy is in a contraction. If real GDP declines for two quarters in a row, the economy is in a **recession**. (A quarter equals three months, or one-quarter of a year.)
3. *Trough.* The low point in real GDP is the trough of a business cycle. This point occurs just before real GDP begins to turn up.
4. *Recovery.* The recovery is the period when real GDP is rising. It begins at the trough and ends at the initial peak.
5. *Expansion.* The expansion refers to increases in real GDP beyond the recovery.

An entire business cycle is measured from peak to peak. (See Exhibit 12-7 on page 359 of your textbook.)

Forecasting Business Cycles

Economists have found signals that indicate the health and sickness of the economy. These signs are called leading indicators, coincident indicators, and lagging indicators.

A *leading indicator* should rise before an upturn in real GDP. It should fall before a downturn in real GDP.

A *coincident indicator* should reach its high point at the same time as a peak of a business cycle. It should reach its low point with the trough of a business cycle.

A *lagging indicator* should reach its high sometime after the peak of a business cycle. It should reach its low sometime after the trough of a business cycle.

What Causes the Business Cycle?

Since the end of World War II, the United States has gone through 10 business cycles. Different economists identify different causes of business cycles.

Money Supply

Some economists believe that changes in the money supply cause the ups and downs in business cycles. They say that when the monetary authorities or the Fed increase the money supply, the economy expands. Then, when the monetary authorities or the Fed decrease the money supply, the economy contracts.

Business Investment, Residential Construction, and Government Spending

Some economists say that business cycles are caused by changes in business investment, residential construction, or government spending. If firms cut back on buying factories and machinery, the economy contracts. If contractors stop building as much, the economy contracts. If government cuts spending substantially, the economy contracts. On the other hand, if either the business sector or government increases spending, the economy could expand.

Politics

Some economists believe that some business cycles have been caused by politicians trying to get reelected to office.

Politicians know that they have a better chance of being reelected if the economy is in good shape. So, they pass more spending bills in Congress, hoping to increase aggregate demand in the economy. They believe that with greater aggregate demand, firms sell more goods and services and hire more workers. When times are good, voters are more likely to reward the people in office who (they believe) made this possible.

However, after the election, the politicians realize that the increase in aggregate demand could lead to inflation. So Congress may then reverse its strategy. However, if Congress cuts spending too much in its attempt to avoid inflation, then the economy could slide into a contraction.

Innovation

Some economists believe that major innovations are the seeds of business cycles. When a company has a new product, other companies need to invest more in their products to stay competitive. The higher spending leads to an expansion. In time, investment tends to slow, and the economy contracts.

Supply Shocks

Some economists argue that major reductions in the supply side cause economies to contract. For example, a war can destroy factories and people; with fewer factories and workers, the economy cannot produce as much. A conflict in the Middle East could cause a major cutback in oil production. Oil is an important resource in the production process. With less oil, the economy cannot produce as much. Firms end up producing less, so they fire some of their workers. Real GDP goes down, and the unemployment rate goes up.

Answer questions 1–4 in the Section 2 Assessment on page 363 of your textbook.

CHAPTER 12, SECTION 3
Outlining Activity

Look through the chapter for an overview of the material. Pay attention to the main topics in the book. As you scan each section of the book, fill in the missing words in the following outline.

I. What Is Economic Growth?

    A. Economic growth refers either to _____ real economic growth or to _____ real economic growth.

    B. Absolute real economic growth is a(n) _____ in _____ from one period to the next.

    C. Per capita real economic growth is an increase from one period to the next in _____, which is real GDP divided by population.

$$\text{Per capita real GDP} = \frac{\text{Real GDP}}{\text{Population}}$$

II. Per Capita Real GDP Growth and the Rule of 70

    A. The Rule of 70 says that the way to find out the time required for any variable to _____ is to divide its percentage growth rate into _____.

$$\text{Rule of 70} = \frac{70}{\text{Growth rate}} = \text{Number of years for a variable to double}$$

III. Economic Growth and a Production Possibilities Frontier

    A. A production possibilities frontier (PPF) shows all possible _____ of two goods that an economy can produce in a certain period of time.

    B. Economic growth can come from a position _____ the PPF. At this point, some _____ in the economy are unused.

    C. Economic growth can come from a position _____ the PPF. In this case, an economy can experience economic growth by shifting its PPF to the _____.

IV. What Causes Economic Growth?

A. With more _____, a country can produce more goods and services.

B. With more _____ , a country can produce more output. However, the _____ of _____ is more important than the quantity of labor.

> Labor productivity = $\dfrac{\text{Total output produced}}{\text{Total hours it takes to produce total output}}$

C. Capital _____ can increase _____ productivity and therefore increase output or real GDP.

D. _____ consists of the knowledge and skill that people obtain from education, training, and work experience. Increases in human capital can lead to economic growth.

E. _____ advances make it possible to obtain more output from the same amount of resources.

F. _____ to produce and innovate help create economic growth.

V. Two Worries About Future Economic Growth

A. More economic growth may come with more _____, more factories, more crowded cities, more emphasis on material goods, and so on.

B. More economic and population growth may hasten the time when the world runs out of resources.

VI. Evaluating Data for Bias

A. Always evaluate and analyze economic information to identify any existing bias.

B. Consider point of view and frame of reference when you look for bias in presented data.

CHAPTER 12, SECTION 3

Just the Facts Handout

What Is Economic Growth?

Absolute real economic growth is an increase in real GDP from one period to the next. For example, suppose real GDP was $10.2 trillion in year 1 and $11.1 trillion in year 2. The economy experienced absolute real economic growth.

Per capita real economic growth is an increase in per capita real GDP from one period to the next. (Per capita real GDP is real GDP divided by population.) For example, suppose per capita real GDP is $23,000 in year 1 and $25,000 in year 2. The economy experienced per capita real economic growth.

Per Capita Real GDP Growth and the Rule of 70

The Rule of 70 can help you find out the time required for any variable to double. Just divide 70 by the percentage growth rate of the variable (expressed as a whole number, not a decimal).

For example, suppose you earn an annual interest rate of 5 percent on a savings account. You want to know how many years it will take for the money you put into the account to double. It will take 14 years because 70 divided by 5 is 14.

Economic Growth and a Production Possibilities Frontier

A production possibilities frontier (PPF) shows all possible combinations of two goods that an economy can produce in a certain period of time. We can show what absolute real economic growth looks like by using a PPF. Economic growth can occur from a position below the PPF, or it can occur from a position on the PPF. (See Exhibit 12-9 on page 366 of your textbook.)

Economic Growth from a Position Below the PPF
Suppose an economy is located at a point below its PPF. At this point, some resources in the economy remain unused. All resources are fully used only when an economy is located on its PPF.

Now suppose the economy moves from a point below its PPF to a point on its PPF. It has experienced economic growth. More of both goods are produced at a point on the PPF than at a point below the PPF. This means that real GDP is higher at a point on the PPF.

Economic Growth from a Position on the PPF
Suppose an economy is located at a point on its PPF. How can an economy that is currently on its PPF experience economic growth? Only by shifting its PPF to the right.

What Causes Economic Growth?

A number of factors can affect a country's economic growth. Some of those factors are natural resources, labor, capital, human capital, technological advances, and incentives.

Natural Resources
With more natural resources, a country can produce more goods and services. Suppose two countries, A and B, are the same in nearly every way. However, A has more natural resources than B has. A is likely to have more economic growth than B.

Labor

With more labor, a country can produce more output. More important to economic growth is the productivity of the labor. Labor productivity is the total output produced divided by the number of hours it takes to produce the output. An increase in labor productivity increases output. This leads to economic growth.

Capital

Capital goods include factories and machinery. Investment in capital goods can lead to increases in labor productivity. And an increase in labor productivity increases output or real GDP. To increase investment in capital goods, a country must reduce present consumption.

Human Capital

Human capital consists of the knowledge and skill that people get from education, on-the-job training, and work experience. The more human capital that the people of a country have, the greater the country's economic growth. Some countries that lack natural resources have still managed to experience economic growth. They have grown their economies by relying on workers who are well trained, educated, and hardworking.

Technological Advances

Technological advances make it possible to get more output from the same amount of resources. Technological advances may be the result of new capital goods or of new ways of producing goods.

Incentives

Some economists have argued that economic growth first developed where people were given the incentive to produce and innovate. Individuals take more risks and work harder when they have an incentive to do so. Being able to keep the money they earn provides people with this incentive.

Two Worries About Future Economic Growth

One worry about economic growth concerns the costs of growth. Some people argue that more economic growth means more pollution, more factories, more crowded cities, and so on. Other people say that no evidence exists to indicate that economic growth causes any or all of these problems. They argue that growth brings many positive things, such as more wealth, more support for the arts, and more protection for the environment.

The second worry concerns the world's resources. Some people believe that more growth in the economy may cause the world to run out of resources sooner. These people urge policies that will slow growth and take care of what we have. Critics of this position argue that these "doomsday forecasts" are based on unrealistic assumptions, oversights, and flimsy evidence.

Evaluating Data for Bias

When you come across any economic information—whether it be economic data, an economic explanation, or an economic theory—it is always a good rule to evaluate and analyze for accuracy and bias. Consider the fact that sometimes the point of view, or frame of reference, of the person presenting the explanation can tilt you in a direction of believing something that may not be true.

Answer questions 1–4 in the Section 3 Assessment on page 371 of your textbook.

Name: _____ Date: _____

CHAPTER 12

Graphic Organizer Activity

Supply the missing words in the blank spaces of these graphic organizers.

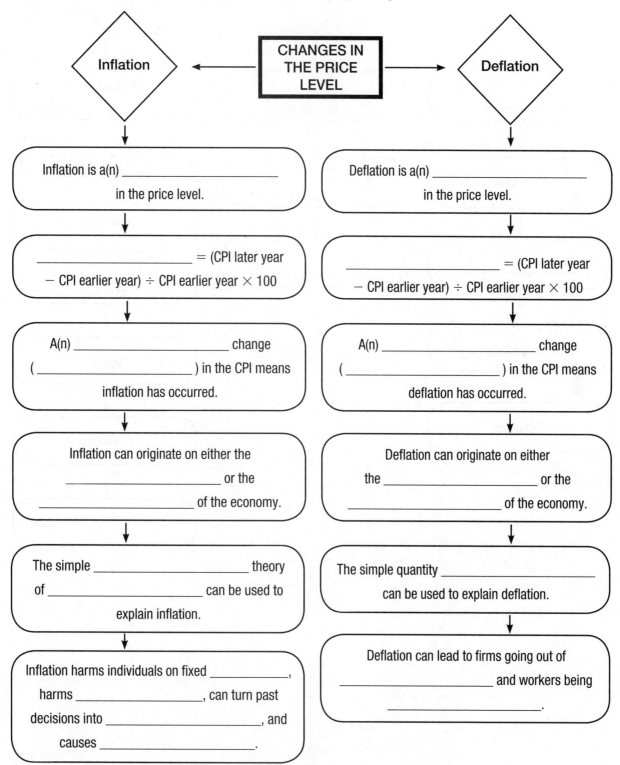

CHANGES IN THE PRICE LEVEL

Inflation

Deflation

Inflation is a(n) _____ in the price level.

Deflation is a(n) _____ in the price level.

_____ = (CPI later year − CPI earlier year) ÷ CPI earlier year × 100

_____ = (CPI later year − CPI earlier year) ÷ CPI earlier year × 100

A(n) _____ change (_____) in the CPI means inflation has occurred.

A(n) _____ change (_____) in the CPI means deflation has occurred.

Inflation can originate on either the _____ or the _____ of the economy.

Deflation can originate on either the _____ or the _____ of the economy.

The simple _____ theory of _____ can be used to explain inflation.

The simple quantity _____ can be used to explain deflation.

Inflation harms individuals on fixed _____, harms _____, can turn past decisions into _____, and causes _____.

Deflation can lead to firms going out of _____ and workers being _____.

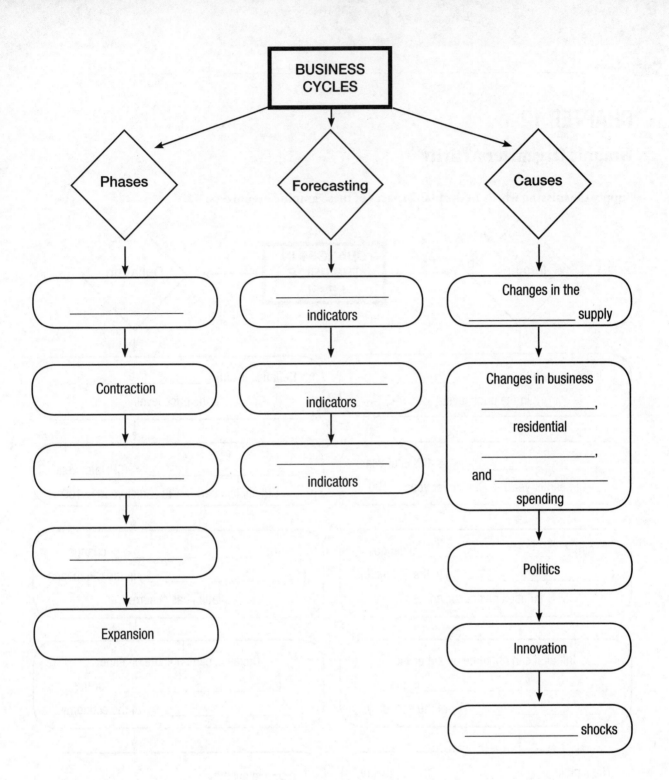

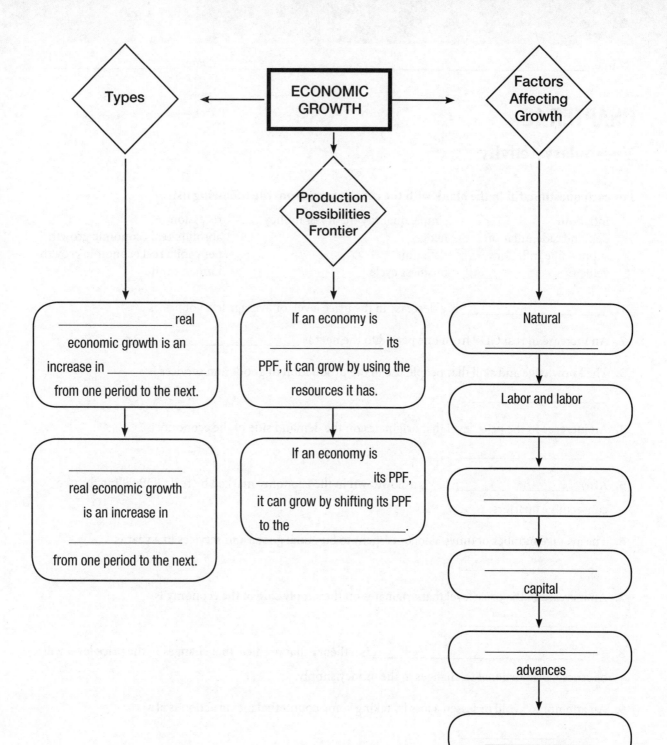

Types

ECONOMIC GROWTH

Factors Affecting Growth

Production Possibilities Frontier

_____ real economic growth is an increase in _____ from one period to the next.

_____ real economic growth is an increase in _____ from one period to the next.

If an economy is _____ its PPF, it can grow by using the resources it has.

If an economy is _____ its PPF, it can grow by shifting its PPF to the _____.

Natural _____

Labor and labor _____

_____

capital

_____ advances

_____

CHAPTER 12
Vocabulary Activity

For each question, fill in the blank with the correct term from the following list.

inflation	simple quantity theory of money	recession
demand-side inflation	hedge	absolute real economic growth
supply-side inflation	deflation	per capita real economic growth
velocity	business cycle	human capital

1. _____ is a decrease in the price level, or average level of prices.

2. An increase in real GDP from one period to the next is _____.

3. The knowledge and skill that people use in the production of goods and services is

   _____.

4. An increase in the price level that originates on the demand side of the economy is

   _____.

5. A(n) _____ is a slowdown in the economy marked by real GDP falling for two

   consecutive quarters.

6. The average number of times a dollar is spent to buy final goods and services in a year is

   _____.

7. An increase in the price level that originates on the supply side of the economy is

   _____.

8. The _____ is a theory that predicts that changes in the price level will

   be strictly proportional to changes in the money supply.

9. An attempt to avoid or lessen a loss by taking some counterbalancing action is a(n)

   _____.

10. A(n) _____ is recurrent swings (up and down) in real GDP.

11. _____ is an increase in the price level, or average level of prices.

12. An increase from one period to the next in per capita real GDP, which is real GDP divided by

    population, is _____.

CHAPTER 12

Working with Graphs and Tables Activity

Use the graph to answer the questions. Write your answers on the lines provided.

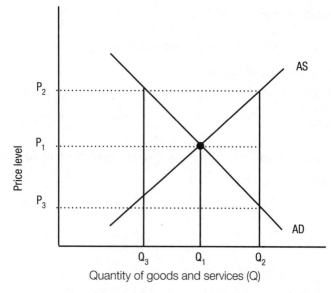

1. The equilibrium price level is _____. The equilibrium quantity of goods and services is _____.

2. If the Fed increases the money supply, the _____ shifts to the _____. The price level _____, and the quantity of goods and services produced _____.

3. If an advancement in technology lowers the costs for firms to produce goods and services, the _____ shifts to the _____. The price level _____, and the quantity of goods and services produced _____.

4. For the event described in question 2, does inflation or deflation occur? Explain your answer.

   _____

   _____

5. For the event described in question 3, does inflation or deflation occur? Explain your answer.

   _____

   _____

CHAPTER 12

Practice Test

Multiple Choice

Circle the letter of the correct answer.

1. Which of the following theories is used to explain inflation?

    a. the simple quantity theory of money
    b. the exchange equation theory
    c. the inflation theory
    d. the velocity theory

2. You put $5,000 in a savings account that pays an annual interest rate of 10 percent. How many years will it take for your savings to double?

    a. 10 years
    b. 7.2 years
    c. 1 year
    d. 72 years

3. Which of the following is *not* usually said to cause the business cycle?

    a. change in the money supply
    b. change in business investment
    c. politics
    d. demand shock

4. What happens if aggregate demand increases by more than aggregate supply increases?

    a. We have deflation.
    b. The price level decreases.
    c. We have inflation.
    d. Velocity decreases.

5. If the CPI is 130 in year 1 and 173 in year 2, what is the inflation rate between the two years?

    a. 6.2 percent
    b. 33.1 percent
    c. 24.9 percent
    d. 16.2 percent

6. If per capita real GDP is $500 and population is 1 million, then what is real GDP?

    a. $5 million
    b. $50 million
    c. $500 million
    d. $100,000 million

7. In which phase of the business cycle is real GDP at its low point?

   a. peak
   b. recovery
   c. contraction
   d. trough

8. You are stranded on a desert island and realize that to survive you must pick bananas and catch fish.

   Which of the following would cause your production possibilities frontier to shift inward?

   a. You make a net for catching fish.
   b. A hurricane destroys many banana trees on the island.
   c. You discover an additional forest of banana trees.
   d. You find a partner to help you catch fish and pick bananas.

True or False

For each of these statements, place a T in the blank if the statement is true or an F if the statement is false.

1. _____ If aggregate demand decreases at the same time that aggregate supply decreases, then the price level and the quantity of goods and services will increase.

2. _____ A leading economic indicator can be used to predict or forecast business cycles.

3. _____ Both inflation and deflation can be caused by changes in aggregate supply and aggregate demand.

4. _____ Inflation raises the standard of living of people on fixed incomes.

5. _____ A leading economic indicator should reach its high point at the same time as a peak of a business cycle and reach its low point with the trough.

Short Answer

Write your answers on the lines provided.

1. How can a country increase its labor productivity? Why would a country want to increase its labor productivity?

   _____

   _____

   _____

   _____

2. How can changes in the money supply cause inflation or deflation? Explain your answer in terms of the simple quantity theory of money.

_____

_____

_____

_____

_____

3. What are the effects of inflation? In your answer, explain who is hurt by inflation.

_____

_____

_____

_____

4. If inflation is a bad thing, then is deflation a good thing? Explain your answer.

_____

_____

_____

_____

CHAPTER 13, SECTION 1

Outlining Activity

Look through the chapter for an overview of the material. Pay attention to the main topics in the book. As you scan each section of the book, fill in the missing words in the following outline.

I. Two Types of Fiscal Policy

A. _____ fiscal policy is an increase in _____ or a reduction in _____ (or both). It is an attempt to increase total spending in the economy in order to reduce the _____ rate.

B. _____ fiscal policy is a decrease in _____ or an increase in _____ (or both). It is an attempt to reduce total spending in the economy in order to reduce _____.

II. Expansionary Fiscal Policy and the Problem of Unemployment

A. A(n) _____ unemployment rate results from people not _____ enough money in the economy.

B. To reduce the unemployment rate, Congress should implement _____ fiscal policy by _____ government _____, _____ taxes, or both.

C. A(n) _____ in government spending means _____ spending in the economy.

D. As a result of the _____ in total spending, firms _____ more goods.

E. When firms start to sell more goods, they have to hire _____ workers to produce the additional goods. The unemployment rate goes _____ as a result of _____ people working.

III. The Issue of Crowding Out

A. _____ occurs when increases in government spending lead to reductions in private spending (by consumers and businesses).

B. Because government spends _____ on goods and services, people need to spend _____.

C. _____ occurs when each dollar _____ in government spending is matched by a dollar _____ in private spending.

D. If _____ occurs, then a(n) _____ in government spending does not raise total spending and does not affect unemployment.

E. _____ occurs when a(n) _____ in private spending only partially offsets a(n) _____ in government spending.

F. If _____ occurs, then a(n) _____ in government spending does raise total spending in the economy.

IV. Contractionary Fiscal Policy and the Problem of Inflation

A. Inflation is the result of _____ spending in the economy.

B. To reduce prices, Congress should implement _____ fiscal policy by _____ government _____, _____ taxes, or both.

C. A(n) _____ in government spending will lead to _____ overall spending in the economy.

D. As a result of the _____ in total spending, firms initially sell fewer goods.

E. As a result of selling fewer goods, firms have surplus goods on hand. To get rid of their surplus goods, firms _____ prices.

V. Fiscal Policy and John Maynard Keynes

A. _____ wrote one of the most influential economic treatises of all time.

B. Keynes disagreed with the classical school of economics. The classical school view said the economy was _____.

C. He believed that the _____ could not always heal itself when it was sick.

D. When the economy cannot recover on its own, Keynes believed that the government should enact a(n) _____ to stimulate spending. The government's job is to increase its spending so that aggregate demand will rise, which will pull the economy out of its sickly state.

VI. Fiscal Policy and Taxes

A. How Taxes Can Affect the Spending (Demand) Side of the Economy

    1. After-tax income is the income people have left over after paying their

    _____.

    2. If the government lowers taxes, then people's after-tax income _____.

    3. As after-tax income rises, people have _____ money to spend on goods and services.

    4. Total spending in the economy _____ as a result of the tax cut.

    5. Firms sell _____ goods and so they hire _____ workers.

    6. Things work in the opposite direction for tax increases.

B. How Taxes Can Affect the Producing (Supply) Side of the Economy

    1. The _____ your after-tax income, the _____ you are willing to work. The _____ your after-tax income, the _____ you are willing to work.

    2. The supply of goods and services in the economy will be _____ (AS curve shifts to the _____) when taxes are _____ than when they are _____.

C. Tax Rates and Tax Revenues

    1. Tax rate _____ can lead to lower or higher tax

    _____.

> Tax revenue = Average tax rate × Income

    2. Tax rate cuts encourage people to work more. In some cases, they may work so much more that tax revenues _____.

    3. _____ believe that _____ in high tax rates can generate _____ tax revenues whereas cuts in low tax rates generate lower tax revenues.

    4. The _____ illustrates the relationship that some economists believe exists between tax rates and tax revenues.

CHAPTER 13, SECTION 1

Just the Facts Handout

Two Types of Fiscal Policy

Fiscal policy deals with government spending and taxes. **Expansionary fiscal policy** is an increase in government spending, a reduction in taxes, or both. The goal of expansionary fiscal policy is to reduce the unemployment rate by increasing total spending in the economy.

    Contractionary fiscal policy is a decrease in government spending, an increase in taxes, or both. The goal of contractionary fiscal policy is to reduce inflation by decreasing total spending in the economy.

Expansionary Fiscal Policy and the Problem of Unemployment

Some economists say that the government should use expansionary fiscal policy to lower the unemployment rate. These economists say that the unemployment rate is high because people are not spending enough money. They explain how expansionary fiscal policy will reduce the unemployment rate as follows:

- Congress should increase government spending, lower taxes, or both. Assume Congress increases government spending.
- If government increases spending, then total spending in the economy will increase.
- As a result of the increase in total spending, firms will sell more goods.
- When firms start to sell more goods, they will have to hire more workers to produce the additional goods.
- Because more people are working, the unemployment rate goes down.

The Issue of Crowding Out

Some economists say that total spending may not increase when government spends more because crowding out can occur. **Crowding out** occurs when increases in government spending lead to reductions in private spending. (Private spending is spending made in the private sector by consumers and businesses.)

    In complete crowding out, each dollar increase in government spending is matched by a dollar decrease in private spending. In this case, an increase in government spending does not lead to an increase in total spending in the economy. Thus, it does not affect the unemployment rate.

    In incomplete crowding out, each dollar increase in government spending is matched by less than a dollar decrease in private spending. In this case, the increase in government spending raises total spending in the economy. As a result, it helps to lower the unemployment rate.

Contractionary Fiscal Policy and the Problem of Inflation

Some economists say that the government should use contractionary fiscal policy to lower the inflation rate. These economists say that inflation results when people buy more than the economy can produce. They say contractionary fiscal policy can reduce the inflation rate as follows:

- Congress should decrease government spending, raise taxes, or both. Assume Congress decreases government spending.

- If government decreases spending, total spending in the economy will decrease.
- As a result of the decrease in total spending, firms initially will sell fewer goods.
- When firms sell fewer goods, they end up with a surplus of goods on hand. They end up with more goods in their warehouses and factories than they want.
- To get rid of their surplus goods, firms lower prices.
- Because prices are lower, the inflation rate goes down.

Fiscal Policy and John Maynard Keynes

John Maynard Keynes was born on June 5, 1883 in England, and died on April 21, 1946. His father was John Neville Keynes, an eminent economist.

In 1936, Keynes published his major work, *The General Theory of Employment, Interest and Money*. Many economists consider this piece of work to be one of the most influential economic treatises ever written.

Keynes believed that the view of the classical school of economics contained errors. The classical school view said the economy is self-regulating. A self-regulating economy is one that can "heal itself" if it "gets sick." If an economy slips into a recession and unemployment begins to rise, there is no need to do anything.

Keynes believed that an economy cannot always heal itself. Sometimes an economy gets sick and cannot get well on its own. When the economy cannot recover on its own the government should step in and enact an expansionary fiscal policy. The government's job is to increase its spending so that aggregate demand will rise, which will pull the economy out of its sickly state.

Keynes has his critics. Not all economists believe that Keynes's diagnosis and recommended treatment are correct.

Fiscal Policy and Taxes

Fiscal policy deals with taxes as well as with government spending. Besides changing its spending, government can also change taxes. Tax changes can affect the spending (demand) side of the economy. They can also affect the producing (supply) side of the economy.

How Taxes Can Affect the Spending (Demand) Side of the Economy

The part of income that people have left after paying taxes is **after-tax income**. If the government lowers taxes, then after-tax income rises. Households have more money, and consumption rises. (Recall that spending by the household sector of the economy is called consumption.) If no other sector of the economy changes its spending, then total spending in the economy rises.

As a result of the increase in total spending, firms will sell more goods. When firms start to sell more goods, they will have to hire more workers to produce the additional goods. Because more people are working, the unemployment rate goes down.

A rise in taxes has the opposite effect. The tax increase will lower after-tax income, thus reducing consumption. The reduction in consumption will lower total spending in the economy, thus lowering the inflation rate.

How Taxes Can Affect the Producing (Supply) Side of the Economy

The higher your after-tax income, the more you are willing to work. The lower your after-tax income, the less you are willing to work. We would expect people to work longer hours and to work harder when the average income tax rate is 20 percent than when it is 70 percent. This increase in labor productivity will increase the supply of goods and services in the economy. (The aggregate supply curve will shift to the right.) So, the supply of goods and services should be greater when taxes are lower than when taxes are higher.

Tax Rates and Tax Revenues

Many people think that a cut in the tax rates will result in lower tax revenues for the government. However, this is not necessarily true. Tax rate cuts can lead to lower or to higher tax revenues.

If income rises by a higher percentage than the percentage that taxes are cut, then tax revenues will be higher after the tax cut. For example, if taxes are cut 10 percent and income rises 12 percent, then tax revenues will rise. If income rises by a smaller percentage than the percentage that taxes are cut, then tax revenues will be lower after the tax cut. For example, if taxes are cut 12 percent and income rises 10 percent, then tax revenues will fall.

Supply-side economists believe that cuts in high tax rates can generate higher tax revenues. On the other hand, cuts in low tax rates generate lower tax revenues. The **Laffer curve** illustrates the relationship that these economists believe exists between tax rates and tax revenues. According to the Laffer curve, as tax rates rise from zero, tax revenues rise. Tax revenues reach a maximum at some point, and then fall with further increases in tax rates. (See Exhibit 13-2 on page 387 of your textbook.)

Answer questions 1–5 in the Section 1 Assessment on page 387 of your textbook.

CHAPTER 13, SECTION 2

Outlining Activity

Look through the chapter for an overview of the material. Pay attention to the main topics in the book. As you scan each section of the book, fill in the missing words in the following outline.

I. Two Types of Monetary Policy

A. Monetary policy deals with changes in the _____ supply.

B. The objective of _____ monetary policy is to _____ total spending in the economy in order to reduce the unemployment rate.

C. The objective of _____ monetary policy is to _____ total spending in the economy in order to reduce inflation.

II. Expansionary Monetary Policy and the Problem of Unemployment

A. The Fed _____ the money supply.

B. A(n) _____ money supply is usually associated with _____ total spending in the economy.

C. As a result of the _____ in spending in the economy, firms begin to sell _____ products.

D. As firms sell _____ products, they have to hire _____ workers, thus _____ the unemployment rate.

E. The issue of _____ does not arise with monetary policy.

III. Contractionary Monetary Policy and the Problem of Inflation

A. The Fed _____ the money supply.

B. A(n) _____ money supply is usually associated with _____ total spending in the economy.

C. As a result of the _____ in spending in the economy, firms begin to sell _____.

D. As firms sell _____ products, their inventories _____. To get rid of surplus goods, firms _____ prices.

IV. Monetary Policy and the Exchange Equation

A. Some economists say that the objective of _____ policy is to maintain a stable _____.

B. The _____, M × V = P × Q, can be written as %ΔM + %ΔV = %ΔP + %ΔQ, where Δ stands for "change in."

C. By rearranging the exchange equation, we can find out how to calculate the percentage change in the _____ supply.

$$\%\Delta M = \%\Delta P + \%\Delta Q - \%\Delta V$$

D. Some economists say that monetary policy should raise the _____ so that the _____ does not change.

E. The Fed should compute the average annual percentage change in V and in Q, set the percentage change in P equal to _____, and calculate the percentage change in M.

V. A Gold Standard as Monetary Policy and the Value of the Dollar

A. Increases and decreases in the money supply are mostly caused by the _____.

B. Some economists advocate a gold standard and believe that it would stabilize the country's money supply.

C. A gold standard ties the (paper) money supply to the supply of gold that a _____ holds.

D. By stabilizing the price of gold, it's also possible to stabilize the general price level, since the general price level moves up and down with the price of gold.

CHAPTER 13, SECTION 2

Just the Facts Handout

Two Types of Monetary Policy

Monetary policy deals with changes in the money supply. **Expansionary monetary policy** is an increase in the money supply. The goal of expansionary monetary policy is to reduce the unemployment rate by increasing total spending in the economy.

 Contractionary monetary policy is a decrease in the money supply. The goal of contractionary monetary policy is to reduce inflation by decreasing total spending in the economy.

Expansionary Monetary Policy and the Problem of Unemployment

Many economists believe expansionary monetary policy lowers the unemployment rate. They explain the process as follows:
- The Fed increases the money supply.
- A greater money supply usually means greater total spending in the economy. (There is more money to spend.)
- As a result of the increase in total spending, firms will sell more goods.
- When firms start to sell more goods, they will have to hire more workers to produce the additional goods.
- Because more people are working, the unemployment rate goes down.

 The issue of crowding out does not arise in monetary policy. If the Fed increases the money supply, no one has to spend less. There is simply more money to spend.

 Because crowding out is not an issue with expansionary monetary policy, many economists argue that increasing the money supply will lower the unemployment rate.

Contractionary Monetary Policy and the Problem of Inflation

Many economists believe contractionary monetary policy reduces inflation. They explain the process as follows:
- The Fed decreases the money supply.
- A smaller money supply is usually associated with lower total spending in the economy. (There is less money to spend.)
- As a result of the decrease in total spending, firms will begin to sell fewer goods.
- When firms sell fewer goods, the inventories in their warehouses rise.
- To get rid of their surplus goods, firms lower prices.
- Because prices are lower, the inflation rate goes down.

Monetary Policy and the Exchange Equation

Some economists say that the goal of monetary policy is to maintain a stable price level. In other words, in terms of the exchange equation ($M \times V = P \times Q$), the goal of monetary policy is to keep P constant.

 The exchange equation can be written as $\%\Delta M + \%\Delta V = \%\Delta P + \%\Delta Q$, where Δ stands for "change in." In other words, the percentage change in the money supply plus the percentage change in velocity equals the percentage change in the price level plus the percentage change in the quantity of goods and services. To calculate the percentage change in the money supply, we can subtract %ΔV from both sides. This gives us %ΔM = %ΔP + %ΔQ − %ΔV.

We want prices to be stable. Prices are stable if the price level does not change. In other words, prices are stable if %ΔP = 0. If %ΔV = 1% and %ΔQ = 3%, then we can find what the percentage change in the money should be as follows:

$$
\begin{aligned}
\%\Delta M &= \%\Delta P + \%\Delta Q - \%\Delta V \\
&= 0\% + 3\% - 1\% \\
&= 2\%
\end{aligned}
$$

So the Fed should increase the money supply by 2 percent to keep prices stable.

Some economists say that monetary policy should be put on automatic pilot. The Fed should simply compute the average annual change in velocity, compute the average annual change in the quantity of goods and services, set the percentage change in prices equal to 0 percent, and calculate the money supply change accordingly.

A Gold Standard as Monetary Policy and the Value of the Dollar

Instead of allowing the Fed to increase and decrease the money supply, some economists argue that the money supply should be stabilized using a gold standard. The gold standard ties the (paper) money supply to the supply of gold that a government holds. And since the supply of gold (in the world) does not usually increase significantly from year to year, it is usually impossible for the money supply to increase significantly.

By stabilizing the price of gold, it's also possible to stabilize the general price level, since the general price level moves up and down with the price of gold. It follows that if the monetary authority stabilizes the market price of gold at $1,000, it will indirectly be very close to stabilizing the general level of prices throughout the market. This is why some economists argue that a gold standard stabilizes the price level, thus preventing a decline in the value of the dollar.

Answer questions 1–3 in the Section 2 Assessment on page 395 of your textbook.

CHAPTER 13, SECTION 3

Outlining Activity

Look through the chapter for an overview of the material. Pay attention to the main topics in the book. As you scan each section of the book, fill in the missing words in the following outline.

I. Rising Unemployment and Inflation (at the Same Time)

    A. Stagflation is when an economy experiences _____ and high

        _____ at the same time.

    B. Stagflation occurred in the 1970s.

II. How Money Changes Affect the Economy

    A. Most economists agree that changes in the money supply affect both _____

    and the _____ of goods and services but that output is affected before prices.

    B. For example, when the Fed increases the money supply, total spending in the economy

    _____. As a result, firms sell more goods. So they hire more workers and

    produce more _____.

    C. When firms begin to sell more, they do not know at first whether the increase is permanent or

    temporary. Firms wait to raise _____ because they think the increase may

    be _____.

    D. So given an increase in the money supply, output is likely to go up before prices do.

    E. The opposite is also true. When the money supply _____, output is affected

    before prices are affected.

III. What Causes Stagflation?

    A. Some economists believe that stagflation is the result of a _____,

    _____ monetary policy.

    B. The Fed _____ the money supply. This move by the Fed first

    _____ output and then _____ prices.

    C. The _____ money supply causes inflation.

    D. At the same time people are dealing with the _____ inflation, the Fed

    _____ the money supply. As a result, output falls.

    E. Because less output is being produced, _____ people are required to work in

    the factories. So unemployment _____.

CHAPTER 13, SECTION 3

Just the Facts Handout

Rising Unemployment and Inflation (at the Same Time)

For many years, economists believed that inflation and unemployment moved in opposite directions. As the inflation rate increased, the unemployment rate decreased. And as the inflation rate decreased, the unemployment rate increased.

Then in the 1970s, inflation and unemployment began to move in the same direction. They both began to increase. The economy began to experience **stagflation**—the occurrence of inflation and high unemployment at the same time.

How Money Changes Affect the Economy

Some economists believe that stagflation is the result of a **stop-and-go, on-and-off monetary policy.** Before you can understand their position, you need to know how monetary policy affects the economy.

Most economists agree that changes in the money supply affect both prices and the output of goods and services. They also agree that output is affected before prices.

For example, when the Fed increases the money supply, total spending in the economy increases. As a result, firms sell more goods. So they begin to hire more workers and produce more output.

However, firms don't raise prices immediately because they don't know whether the increase in sales is temporary or permanent. Firms don't want to raise prices if the increase is temporary. Suppose they raise prices and the higher sales were not permanent. Then the firms may become less competitive because their new prices are too high.

We conclude that if the money supply increases, output is likely to go up before prices do. In the same way, if the money supply decreases, output is likely to go down before prices do.

What Causes Stagflation?

Some economists believe stagflation is caused by a monetary policy that changes too often. They describe what happens as follows:

- The Fed increases the money supply. At first this raises output, and then it raises prices.
- Time passes. The increased money supply causes inflation.
- The Fed starts worrying about the high inflation. It reduces the money supply. This affects output, and it falls. Because of less output, fewer workers are needed. Unemployment rises.

In this scenario, the earlier monetary policy caused the high inflation and the current monetary policy caused the high unemployment. The economy is experiencing the effects of both monetary policies—stagflation.

Not all economists agree with this description of the cause of stagflation. Also, not all economists believe that this is the only cause. Some economists maintain that a marked decrease in aggregate supply can also cause stagflation. Such a decrease might be due to a fall in the market supply of a major resource, such as oil.

Answer questions 1–4 in the Section 3 Assessment on page 401 of your textbook.

CHAPTER 13

Graphic Organizer Activity

Supply the missing words in the blank spaces of these graphic organizers.

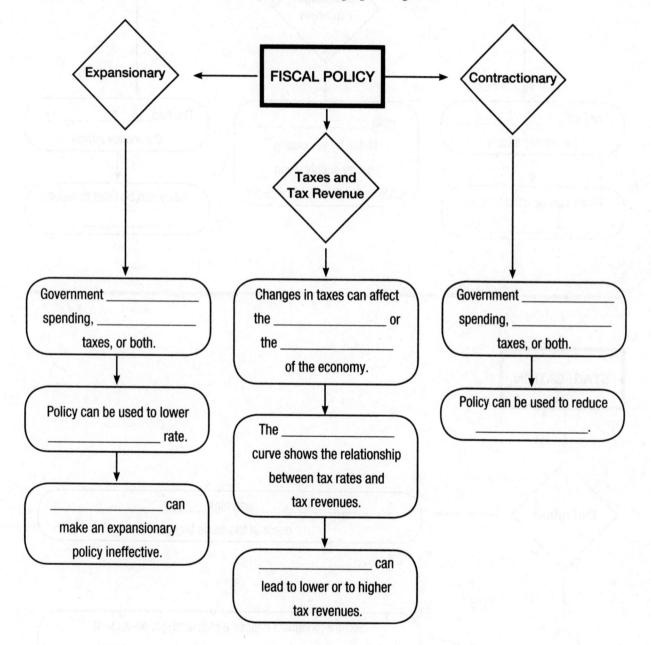

Expansionary ← FISCAL POLICY → Contractionary

Taxes and Tax Revenue

Government _____ spending, _____ taxes, or both.

Policy can be used to lower _____ rate.

_____ can make an expansionary policy ineffective.

Changes in taxes can affect the _____ or the _____ of the economy.

The _____ curve shows the relationship between tax rates and tax revenues.

_____ can lead to lower or to higher tax revenues.

Government _____ spending, _____ taxes, or both.

Policy can be used to reduce _____.

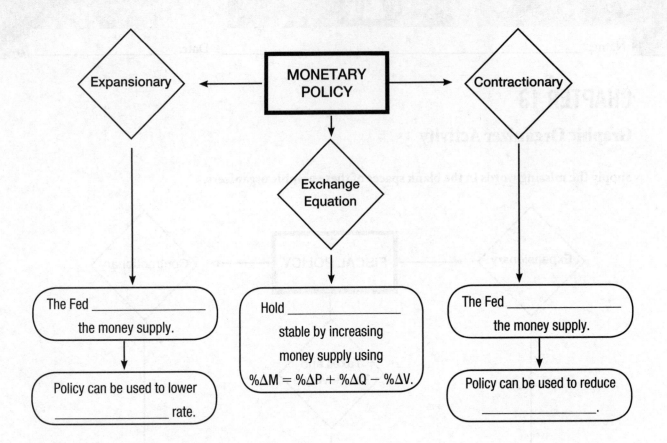

MONETARY POLICY

Expansionary

Contractionary

Exchange Equation

The Fed _____ the money supply.

↓

Policy can be used to lower _____ rate.

Hold _____ stable by increasing money supply using %ΔM = %ΔP + %ΔQ − %ΔV.

The Fed _____ the money supply.

↓

Policy can be used to reduce _____.

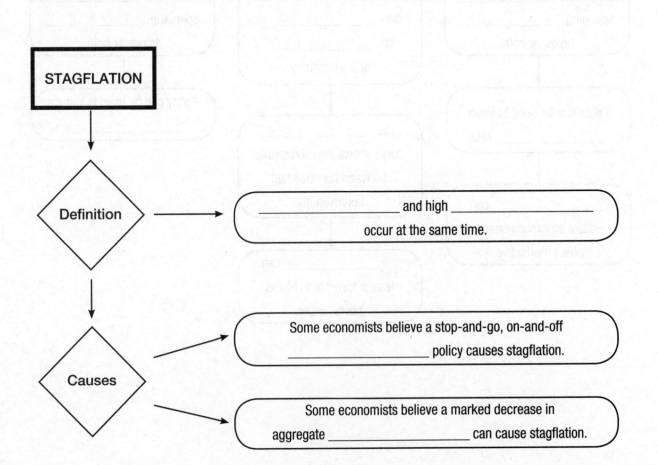

STAGFLATION

↓

Definition → _____ and high _____ occur at the same time.

Causes → Some economists believe a stop-and-go, on-and-off _____ policy causes stagflation.

→ Some economists believe a marked decrease in aggregate _____ can cause stagflation.

Guided Reading and Study Guide

CHAPTER 13
Vocabulary Activity

For each question, fill in the blank with the correct term from the following list.

fiscal policy
expansionary fiscal policy
contractionary fiscal policy
crowding out
after-tax income

Laffer curve
monetary policy
expansionary monetary policy
contractionary monetary
  policy

stagflation
stop-and-go, on-and-off
  monetary policy

1. _____ is a decrease in the money supply.

2. _____ is the occurrence of inflation and high unemployment at the same time.

3. Changes government makes in spending or taxation to achieve particular economic goals is _____.

4. The part of income that's left over after taxes are paid is _____.

5. A(n) _____ is an erratic monetary policy.

6. The situation in which increases in government spending lead to a reduction in private spending is _____.

7. Changes the Fed makes in the money supply is _____.

8. _____ is an increase in government spending or a reduction in taxes.

9. _____ is an increase in the money supply.

10. _____ is a decrease in government spending or an increase in taxes.

11. The _____ shows the relationship between tax rates and tax revenues.

CHAPTER 13

Working with Graphs and Tables Activity

For questions 1 and 2, write your answers on the lines provided. Then complete the table in question 3.

1. The exchange equation is _____, where M is the _____, V is _____, P is the _____, and Q is the _____ .

2. The equation that shows what the percentage change in the money supply equals is

   _____ .

3. Fill in the missing percentages that will maintain price stability.

%ΔM	%ΔQ	%ΔV
	5%	4%
3 %	4%	
	2%	4%
−3%		3%
	3%	−1%

CHAPTER 13

Practice Test

True or False

For each of these statements, place a *T* in the blank if the statement is true or an *F* if the statement is false.

1. _____ If the government lowers taxes the average household has less money to spend on goods and services.

2. _____ Expansionary fiscal policy is the main cause of stagflation.

3. _____ If government spending increases by $1 million and complete crowding out occurs, private spending increases by $1 million.

4. _____ Contractionary monetary policy is a decrease in the money supply by the Fed.

5. _____ Monetary policy refers to changes Congress makes in spending or taxation or both to achieve particular economic goals.

6. _____ Expansionary monetary policy increases the money supply and ultimately decreases the unemployment rate.

7. _____ Contractionary monetary policy can be used to reduce inflation.

8. _____ A reduction in income tax rates leaves more after-tax income for people, so they end up spending more.

9. _____ If $\%\Delta Q = 10\%$ and $\%\Delta V = 3\%$, then the percentage change in the money supply should equal 13 percent in order to keep the price level stable.

10. _____ The Laffer curve shows that two different tax rates can generate the same tax revenues.

11. _____ If expansionary fiscal policy is ineffective at raising total spending in the economy and lowering the unemployment rate, then complete crowding out may have occurred.

12. _____ Contractionary fiscal policy calls for decreasing government spending, or increasing taxes, or both.

Short Answer

Write your answers on the lines provided.

1. Explain how expansionary fiscal policy may reduce unemployment.

_____

_____

_____

2. Explain how contractionary fiscal policy may reduce inflation.

_____

_____

_____

3. Can a tax rate cut ever increase tax revenues? Explain your answer.

_____

_____

_____

4. Suppose you are paid $75,000 as an environmental lawyer. Your income is taxed at a rate of 35 percent. What is your after-tax income? Show your work.

_____

_____

Guided Reading and Study Guide

CHAPTER 14, SECTION 1
Outlining Activity

Look through the chapter for an overview of the material. Pay attention to the main topics in the book. As you scan each section of the book, fill in the missing words in the following outline.

I. Three Major Federal Taxes

    A. The _____ tax is the tax a person pays on his or her income.

    B. The tax corporations pay on their profits is the _____ tax.

    C. The _____ tax is a federal government tax placed on income generated from
    employment. Half of the tax is placed on the employer, and half is placed on
    the employee.

II. Three Other Taxes

    A. _____ taxes are applied to the purchase of a broad range of goods—cars,
    computers, clothes, books, and so on—when they are purchased.

        1. State governments typically raise tax revenue through _____ taxes.
           There is no federal (national) _____ tax.

    B. _____ taxes are taxes placed on the purchase of certain goods.

    C. _____ tax is a tax on the value of property (such as a home). It is a major
    revenue source for state and local governments.

III. Value-Added Tax

    A. Some individuals propose value-added tax as an additional tax while others think that it should replace the _____.

    B. A(n) _____ is a multistage tax that is collected from firms at each stage in the production and distribution process.

IV. _____, _____, _____, and Income Taxes

    A. With a(n) _____ income tax, everyone pays taxes at the same rate, whatever the income level.

    B. With a(n) _____ income tax, people pay at a higher rate as their income levels rise.

    C. With a(n) _____ income tax, people pay at a lower rate as their income levels rise.

V. How Long Do You Have to Work to Pay All Your Taxes?

    A. If a person began work on January 1, 2016, he or she would have to work until _____, before earning enough to pay all taxes owed.

    B. The number of days a person has to work to pay his or her entire tax bill differs between states because taxes are _____ in some states than in other states.

VI. Who Pays What Percentage of Federal Income Taxes?

    A. The top 1 percent of income earners in 2016 earned _____ percent of all U.S. income.

    B. The top 1 percent of income earners paid _____ percent of federal income taxes in 2016.

    C. In 2014, a person who earned $465,626 and a person who earned $10 million were both in the _____ of income earners.

    D. Taxpayers pay a _____ average tax rate as their incomes rise.

CHAPTER 14, SECTION 1

Just the Facts Handout

Three Major Federal Taxes

There are three levels of government: federal, state, and local. At the federal level, the three major taxes are the personal income tax, the corporate income tax, and the social security tax.

- The *personal income tax* is the tax a person pays on his or her income. In addition to the federal personal income tax, many states have a personal income tax.
- The *corporate income tax* is the tax that corporations pay on their profits. The federal government requires corporations to pay a corporate income tax. Many state governments also require this tax.
- The *social security tax* is a federal government tax placed on employment income. Half of the tax is placed on the employer. The other half is placed on the employee.

   The federal government had tax revenues of $3,267 billion in 2016. Of this amount, $1,546 billion came from personal income taxes, $300 billion came from corporate income taxes, and $1,115 billion came from social security taxes.

   About 91 percent of federal government tax revenue was from personal income taxes, corporate income taxes, and social security taxes. About 47 percent was from personal income taxes, about 9.2 percent was from corporate income taxes, and about 34 percent was from social security taxes.

Three Other Taxes

Sales taxes are added to the prices of many goods. State governments typically raise money through sales taxes. The federal government does not collect sales tax.

   Excise taxes are added to the prices of certain goods, such as tobacco products and gasoline. Every time people buy gasoline at a gas station, they pay an excise tax. The federal government and many state governments collect excise taxes.

   Property tax is a tax on the value of property (such as a home). It is a major source of revenue for state and local governments.

Value-Added Tax

Some individuals want a value-added tax added to the list of other taxes that currently exist while others suggest it as a tax that would replace the sales tax. A **value-added tax** is a multistage tax that is collected from firms at each stage in the production and distribution process.

The following illustrates the value-added tax. Firm A, a manufacturer, sells a good to firm B, a wholesaler, for $700. Firm B distributes the good to firm C, a retailer, for $900. The value added by firm B is $200. Firm C sells the good to a customer for $1,000. The value added by firm C is $100. Each firm is taxed on the value it added to the good. Firm A is taxed on $700, firm B is taxed on $200, and firm C is taxed on $100.

Proportional, Progressive, and Regressive Income Taxes

With a **proportional income tax,** everyone pays taxes at the same rate, whatever the income level. Sometimes a proportional income tax is called a flat tax because everyone pays the same flat tax rate.

With a **progressive income tax,** people pay at a higher rate as their income levels rise. The United States has a progressive income tax structure. For example, in 2016, the tax rates were 10, 15, 25, 28, 33, 35, and 39.6 percent.

With a **regressive income tax,** people pay taxes at a lower rate as their income levels rise.

How Long Do You Have to Work to Pay All Your Taxes?

The average person had to work from January 1, 2016, until April 24, 2016, before earning enough to pay all taxes owed. Exhibit 14-5 on page 410 of your textbook shows how long the average taxpayer had to work to pay taxes in selected years. The number of days a person has to work is not the same for all states. This is because taxes are higher in some states than in other states.

Who Pays What Percentage of Federal Income Taxes?

Most people in the United States think that wealthy people do not pay their fair share of taxes. Do you think this is the case? Before you answer, you need to get some idea of what wealthy Americans pay in taxes compared to what they earn in income. Exhibit 14-6 on page 413 of your textbook shows information about income and federal income taxes for various groups of people. As you analyze the information in the exhibit, think about (1) what you mean by "wealthy" and (2) what you mean by a "fair share" of taxes.

Answer questions 1–4 in the Section 1 Assessment on page 413 of your textbook.

CHAPTER 14, SECTION 2
Outlining Activity

Look through the chapter for an overview of the material. Pay attention to the main topics in the book. As you scan each section of the book, fill in the missing words in the following outline.

I. How Does the Federal Government Spend Money?

    A. In 2016, the federal government spent _____ billion on national defense. This amount was _____ percent of total federal government spending that year.

    B. In 2016, the federal government spent _____ billion on income security. This amount was about _____ percent of total federal government spending.

    C. In 2016, the federal government spent $916.1 billion on _____ payments, which largely go to retired persons. This was about _____ percent of total federal government spending.

    D. In 2016, the federal government spent $594.5 billion on _____, which is hospital and medical insurance for social security beneficiaries.

    E. In 2016, the _____ payment on the national debt was approximately $240.7 billion. This was _____ percent of total federal government spending.

II. The Costs and Benefits of Government Spending Programs

    A. Sometimes spending programs are passed in Congress that have greater _____ than _____.

    B. _____ can lead to something being bought even though its total benefits are less than its total costs.

III. The Budget Process

    A. The budget process begins with the president of the United States, who, with others in the _____ branch of government, prepares the budget.

        1. The president's budget recommends to Congress how much should be spent for such things as national defense and income security programs.

2. The president must _____ the budget to Congress on or before the first _____ in February of each year.

B. After the budget is submitted to Congress, members of many congressional _____ and _____ scrutinize it.

   1. The _____ advises the members of the congressional committees and subcommittees on technical details of the budget.

   2. Many details of the budget may be changed to reflect _____ between the president and Congress.

C. Congress is obligated to pass a budget by the beginning of the _____ year. (The fiscal year of the federal government begins on October 1 and runs through September 30.)

D. Once Congress passes the budget, the details of spending outlined in the budget become _____ for that fiscal year.

IV. What Is a Fair Share?

A. The _____ principle holds that a person should pay in taxes an amount equal to the benefits he or she receives from government expenditures.

B. The _____ principle says that people should pay taxes according to their abilities to pay. Because a rich person is more able to pay taxes than a poor person, a rich person should pay more taxes than a poor person.

V. Budgets: Balanced and in Deficit

A. Budget _____ occur when government expenditures exceed tax revenues.

B. A budget _____ exists if tax revenues exceed government expenditures.

C. After the _____, people began to accept budget deficits as a way of reducing unemployment.

D. If the government spends _____ than it receives in _____, it has to borrow the difference and incur a debt.

   1. Every time the federal government runs a deficit, it has to _____ money and incur a debt.

   2. _____ lead to _____. The debt of the federal government is called the _____.

E. When the government borrows money to pay for the excess of its spending over tax revenues, it has to _____ that money from _____.

1. Those people will have to be _____ one day. The _____ has to be paid off.

2. _____ must be used to pay off the debt, so taxes have to be higher than they would have been if there were no debt.

3. Some economists say that for future taxpayers, current budget deficits are a form of "taxation without _____."

CHAPTER 14, SECTION 2

Just the Facts Handout

How Does the Federal Government Spend Money?

In 2016, the federal government spent approximately $3,881.1 billion. The federal government breaks down its spending according to categories.

In 2016, the federal government spent $595.3 billion on national defense. The total amount was about 17.99 percent of total federal government spending.

Income security refers to government programs that help people with housing, food, unemployment, and so on. The federal government spent $514.6 billion on income security in 2016. This amount was about 13.3 percent of total federal government spending.

In 2016, the federal government spent $916.1 billion on social security payments. Most of these payments went to retired persons. These payments were about 23.6 percent of total federal government spending. The federal government also spent $594.5 billion on Medicare. Medicare is hospital and medical insurance for people who receive social security payments. This amount was 15.4 percent of total federal government spending.

Sometimes the federal government spends more money than it receives in tax revenues. Then it has to borrow money. The **national debt** is the total amount of money the federal government owes. In September 2017, the national debt was $20.16 trillion.

The federal government has to pay interest on the money it borrows. In 2013, the government owed about $228.6 billion in interest on the national debt. This was 6.08 percent of total federal government spending.

The Costs and Benefits of Government Spending Programs

Sometimes Congress passes spending programs that have greater costs than benefits. Government decides whether to buy something by voting.

The Budget Process

The president of the United States works with others in the executive branch of government to prepares the budget. The president's budget tells Congress how much should be spent for various things. The president gives the budget to Congress on or before the first Monday in February of each year.

Members of Congress examine the budget. The Congressional Budget Office helps the members understand technical details of the budget.

While the budget is in Congress, the members may disagree with the president about how money should be spent. At this time, public opinion can influence congresspersons. The American people can write or call their representatives and tell them what they think about the budget. Also during this time, special-interest groups may lobby members of Congress and tell Congress what they want out of the budget.

Congress must pass a budget by the beginning of the fiscal year. The fiscal year of the federal government begins October 1 and runs through September 30. (In contrast, the calendar year begins January 1 and runs through December 31.) Once Congress passes the budget, it becomes law for that fiscal year.

What Is a Fair Share?

Most people believe that everyone should pay his or her fair share of taxes. Two principles of taxation look at how to determine a person's fair share.

The benefits-received principle says that a person should pay the same amount in taxes that the person receives from government spending. For example, the government spends money to improve and maintain our roads and highways. Gas tax revenues are used to take care of roads. The more someone uses roads and highways, the more that person pays in gas tax revenues. So, the major users of roads and highways pay most of the costs of keeping up roads and highways.

With some government-provided goods, however, it is not so easy to relate benefits received to taxes paid. For example, almost all Americans benefit from national defense. However, it is hard to figure out how much one person benefits relative to another person. Often, the ability-to-pay principle is used instead of the benefits-received principle.

The ability-to-pay principle says that people should pay taxes according to their abilities to pay. A rich person is more able to pay taxes than a poor person. Therefore, a rich person should pay more taxes than a poor person.

Budgets: Balanced and in Deficit

A **budget deficit** occurs when government spending is greater than tax revenues. A **budget surplus** exists if tax revenues are greater than government spending.

Before the Great Depression (1929 to the early 1940s), most people believed that the federal budget should be balanced. In other words, government spending should equal tax revenues. However, the economic downturn of the Great Depression made people doubt this belief. Many people came to see budget deficits as necessary, given the high unemployment in the economy. According to them, the choice was simple: (1) keep the federal budget balanced and suffer high unemployment (along with reduced output of goods and services) or (2) accept the budget deficit and reduce the unemployment rate.

While running a budget deficit has benefits, it also has costs. Every time the federal government runs a deficit, it has to borrow money and incur a debt. In short, deficits lead to debt. The debt of the federal government is called the national debt. The national debt in September 2017 was $20.16 trillion. The per capita national debt was about $61,320. The per capita national debt is sometimes referred to as each "citizen's share" of the national debt.

When the government borrows money because of budget deficits, it has to borrow that money from people. These people will have to be repaid one day. The debt has to be paid off. Taxes must be used to pay off the government's debt. So, in the future, when the debt has to be repaid, taxes have to be higher than they would have been if there were no debt. According to some economists, current budget deficits are a form of "taxation without representation" for future taxpayers.

Answer questions 1–4 in the Section 2 Assessment on page 425 of your textbook.

CHAPTER 14

Graphic Organizer Activity

Supply the missing words in the blank spaces of these graphic organizers.

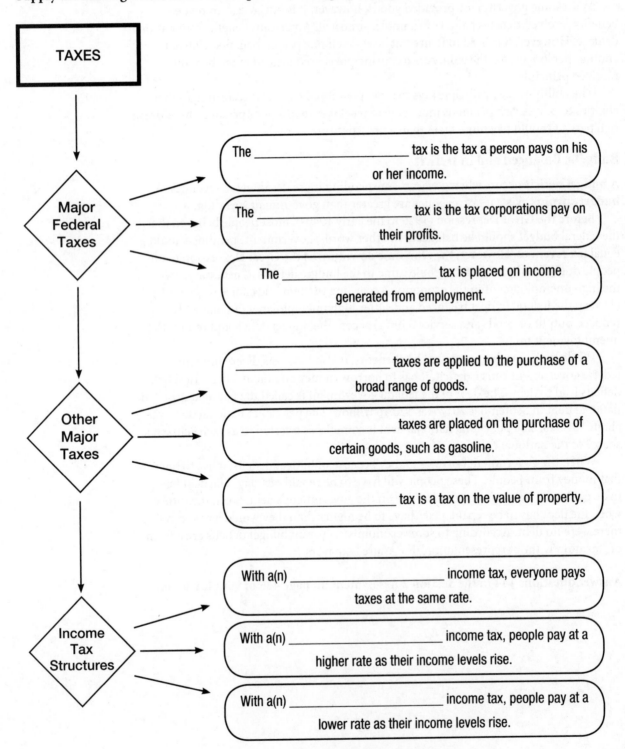

TAXES

Major Federal Taxes

The _____ tax is the tax a person pays on his or her income.

The _____ tax is the tax corporations pay on their profits.

The _____ tax is placed on income generated from employment.

Other Major Taxes

_____ taxes are applied to the purchase of a broad range of goods.

_____ taxes are placed on the purchase of certain goods, such as gasoline.

_____ tax is a tax on the value of property.

Income Tax Structures

With a(n) _____ income tax, everyone pays taxes at the same rate.

With a(n) _____ income tax, people pay at a higher rate as their income levels rise.

With a(n) _____ income tax, people pay at a lower rate as their income levels rise.

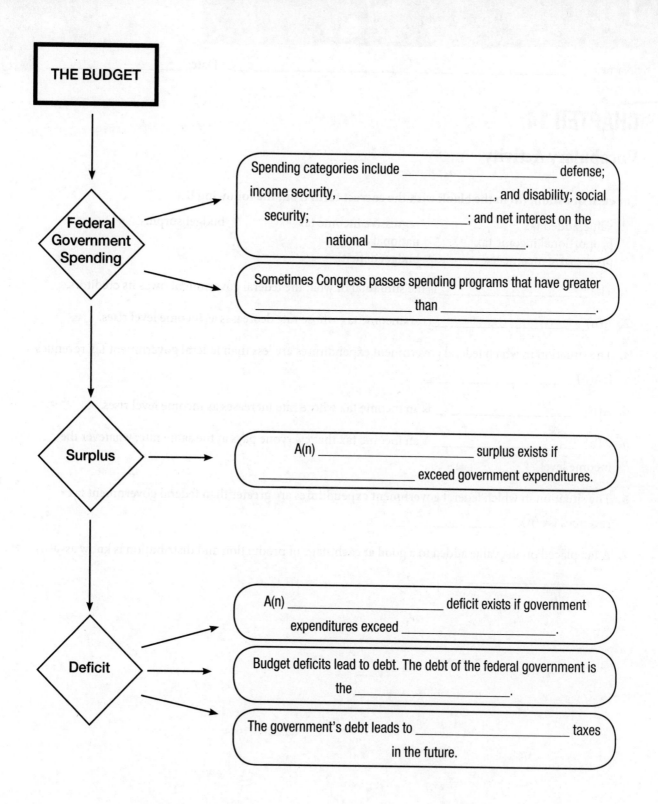

THE BUDGET

Federal Government Spending

Spending categories include _____ defense; income security, _____, and disability; social security; _____; and net interest on the national _____.

Sometimes Congress passes spending programs that have greater _____ than _____.

Surplus

A(n) _____ surplus exists if _____ exceed government expenditures.

Deficit

A(n) _____ deficit exists if government expenditures exceed _____.

Budget deficits lead to debt. The debt of the federal government is the _____.

The government's debt leads to _____ taxes in the future.

CHAPTER 14

Vocabulary Activity

For each question, fill in the blank with the correct term from the following list.

value-added tax   regressive income tax   budget surplus
proportional income tax national debt
progressive income tax budget deficit

1. The _____ is the sum total of what the federal government owes its creditors.

2. A(n) _____ is an income tax whose rate decreases as income level rises.

3. The situation in which federal government expenditures are less than federal government tax revenues is a(n) _____.

4. A(n) _____ is an income tax whose rate increases as income level rises.

5. A(n) _____ is an income tax that everyone pays at the same rate, whatever the income level.

6. The situation in which federal government expenditures are greater than federal government tax revenues is a(n) _____.

7. A tax placed on the value added to a good at each stage of production and distribution is know as a(n) _____

CHAPTER 14
Working with Graphs and Tables Activity

The following diagram shows the budget process from start to finish. Write the correct answers on the lines provided.

The budget process begins with the _____ of the United States. The _____ and others in the _____ of government prepare the budget.

_____ recommends the budget to _____. The budget must be submitted to _____ on or before the _____ in _____ of each year.

Members of many _____ and _____ closely examine the budget.

The _____ advises the members of the committees and subcommittees on any technical details of the president's budget.

The _____ and _____ may disagree about how money should be spent.

While the budget is in _____, many details of the _____ budget may be changed.

These changes reflect _____ between the _____ and _____.

_____ must pass a budget by the beginning of the _____ year, which begins on _____ 1 and runs through _____ 30.

Once _____ the budget, the details of spending outlined in the budget become _____ for that _____ year.

CHAPTER 14

Practice Test

Multiple Choice

Circle the letter of the correct answer.

1. To which of the following are current budget deficits linked?

   a. less current government spending
   b. higher future taxes
   c. higher current unemployment
   d. lower future inflation

2. Which of the following made up the largest percentage of federal government tax revenues in 2013?

   a. corporate income tax
   b. sales tax
   c. social security tax
   d. personal income tax

3. Which of the following says that each person should pay taxes according to the benefits that he or she receives from government expenditures?

   a. ability-to-pay principle
   b. benefits-received principle
   c. progressive principle
   d. proportional principle

4. Which of the following is a federal government tax placed on income from employment?

   a. excise tax
   b. sales tax
   c. personal income tax
   d. social security tax

5. How many days did the average taxpayer have to work in 2016 in order to pay all his or her taxes?

   a. 112 days
   b. 120 days
   c. 115 days
   d. 110 days

6. A person's tax rate decreases as the person's income level rises with which of the following?

   a. proportional income tax
   b. progressive income tax
   c. regressive income tax
   d. excise income tax

7. Which of the following made up the largest percentage of federal government spending in 2013?

    a. national defense and homeland security spending
    b. social security payments
    c. interest payments on the national debt
    d. Medicare spending

8. What exists when government spending is greater than tax revenues?

    a. a budget deficit
    b. a budget surplus
    c. a budget tax
    d. an interest payment

9. What is the sum total of what the federal government owes its creditors called?

    a. national deficit
    b. national debt
    c. president's budget
    d. future taxes

10. Which of the following does everyone pay at the same rate, whatever the income level?

    a. progressive income tax
    b. regressive income tax
    c. proportional income tax
    d. excise income tax

Short Answer

Write your answers on the lines provided.

1. Describe the ways a budget deficit can increase.

    _____

    _____

2. Explain why someone who favors the ability-to-pay principle may also favor a progressive income tax.

    _____

    _____

    _____

    _____

3. What three federal taxes make up almost all of federal tax revenues?

_____

_____

4. Explain the difference between a sales tax and an excise tax.

_____

_____

_____

_____

5. How can a budget deficit today increase taxes for a future generation?

_____

_____

_____

CHAPTER 15, SECTION 1
Outlining Activity

Look through the chapter for an overview of the material. Pay attention to the main topics in the book. As you scan each section of the book, fill in the missing words in the following outline.

I. Why Do People in Different Countries _____ **with Each Other?**

    A. Individuals trade to make themselves _____.

    B. Some countries are able to produce some goods that other countries _____
produce or can produce only at extremely _____.

II. What Are Exports and Imports?

    A. _____ are goods produced in the domestic country and sold to residents of
a foreign country.

    B. _____ are goods produced in foreign countries and purchased by residents
of the domestic country.

III. Balance of Trade

    A. A country's balance of trade is the difference between the value of its _____
and the value of its _____.

> Balance of trade = Value of exports − Value of imports

IV. _____ **and** _____ **Advantage**

    A. When a country can produce more of a good than another country using the same amount of
resources, it is said to have a(n) _____ advantage.

    B. A country may decide to _____ in the production of one good and then
trade some of it for other goods.

    C. When a country has a(n) _____ advantage, it can produce a good at lower
_____ cost than another country.

    D. For example, assume the United States can produce either 150 units of food and 0 units of
clothing or 100 units of food and 25 units of clothing. Also assume Japan can produce either 30
units of food and 120 units of clothing or 0 units of food and 180 units of clothing.

1. To produce _____ additional units of food, the United States must give up _____ units of clothing. In other words, for every 1 extra unit of food, the United States will have to give up _____ unit of clothing. So, the opportunity cost of producing 1 unit of food is _____ unit of clothing.

2. To produce _____ additional units of food, Japan must give up _____ units of clothing. In other words, for every 1 extra unit of food, Japan will have to give up _____ units of clothing. So, the opportunity cost of producing 1 unit of food is _____ units of clothing.

3. The opportunity cost of producing 1 unit of food is _____ unit of clothing for the United States and _____ units of clothing for Japan.

4. The United States has a comparative advantage in _____ production. It should specialize in producing _____.

5. Japan has a comparative advantage in _____ production. It should specialize in producing _____.

V. Benefits of Specialization and Trade

A. If countries _____ in the production of the goods in which they have a comparative advantage and then trade some of these goods for other goods, they can make themselves better off.

VI. Outsourcing and Offshoring

A. _____ describes work done for a company by either another company or by people other than the original company's employees.

B. _____ is when a company outsources certain work to individuals in another country.

1. U.S. companies hire individuals who live in other countries, but foreign companies hire individuals who work in the United States. Offshoring is a _____.

2. The motivation behind offshoring is to lower _____ (and thus raise profits). If _____ are lower, the price of the good will fall. Consumers _____ from paying lower prices.

3. Offshoring is _____ at work.

VII. The _____ of Offshoring Are Easier to See than the _____

    A. It is easy to see the costs of _____ to U.S. workers when U.S. companies decide to hire foreign workers.

    B. It is not so easy to see the Americans who work for _____ companies.

    C. You also don't see the lower _____ that often result from offshoring.

CHAPTER 15, SECTION 1

Just the Facts Handout

Why Do People in Different Countries Trade with Each Other?

People trade to make themselves better off. They may trade on a personal scale. For instance, two people trade because each has something the other person wants. They may also trade on an international scale. For instance, Elaine in the United States trades with Cho in China because Cho has something that Elaine wants and Elaine has something that Cho wants.

Different countries have different climates and resources. So, some countries can produce some goods that other countries cannot produce. Also, some countries can produce some goods much cheaper than other countries can. By trading, countries make themselves better off.

What Are Exports and Imports?

When we discuss international trade, we call our own country the domestic country. We call any other country a foreign country.

Exports are goods that are produced in the domestic country and sold in a foreign country. Major U.S. exports include automobiles, computers, aircraft, corn, wheat, soybeans, scientific instruments, coal, machinery, and plastic materials.

Imports are goods produced in foreign countries and purchased in the domestic country. Major U.S. imports include petroleum, clothing, iron, steel, office machines, footwear, fish, coffee, and diamonds.

Balance of Trade

A country's **balance of trade** is the value of its exports minus the value of its imports. The result of this subtraction can be positive or negative. If a country's balance of trade is positive, the country has a trade surplus. If a country's balance of trade is negative, the country has a trade deficit.

Absolute and Comparative Advantage

Suppose that the United States and Japan both produce food and clothing. Each country can produce different combinations of these two goods. The countries use the same amount of resources to produce each combination of food and clothing. The United States can produce one of these combinations:
- Combination A: 150 units of food and 0 units of clothing, or
- Combination B: 100 units of food and 25 units of clothing.

Japan can produce one of these combinations:
- Combination C: 30 units of food and 120 units of clothing, or
- Combination D: 0 units of food and 180 units of clothing.

A country has an **absolute advantage** if it can produce more of a good with the same amount of resources. In our example, the United States has an absolute advantage in producing food. Japan has an absolute advantage in producing clothing.

Two countries may decide to trade two goods with each other. Then each country may **specialize** in the production of one good. Each country will specialize in producing the good that gives it a comparative advantage. A country has a **comparative advantage** if it can produce the good at a lower opportunity cost than the other country can.

Suppose that the United States and Japan decide to trade with each other. Which good should each specialize in and trade? In other words, which country has a comparative advantage in producing food, and which has a comparative advantage in producing clothing? To answer this question, we have to find the opportunity costs for both goods for both countries.

Suppose the United States produces combination A. It will gain 50 more units of food, but it will lose 25 units of clothing. In other words, for every 1 extra unit of food, it will give up ½ unit of clothing. So for the United States, the opportunity cost of 1 unit of food is ½ unit of clothing.

Suppose Japan produces combination C. It gains 30 more units of food, but it loses 60 units of clothing. So for Japan, the opportunity cost of 1 unit of food is 2 units of clothing.

The United States gives up ½ unit of clothing to produce 1 unit of food. Japan gives up 2 units of clothing to produce 1 unit of food. So the United States has a comparative advantage in food production.

We could follow the same procedure for clothing production. Then we would find that Japan can produce clothing more cheaply than the United States can. So, Japan has a comparative advantage in clothing production.

The United States should specialize in producing food. Japan should specialize in producing clothing. Then the two countries should trade food for clothing.

Benefits of Specialization and Trade

Without specialization and trade, two countries have only what they produce. With specialization, each country can produce more of the good for which it has a comparative advantage. The two countries can then trade some of that good for other goods. With specialization and trade, each country can have more of *all* goods.

Exhibit 15-3 on page 439 of your textbook summarizes the example of trade between the United States and Japan. The two countries decide that the United States will trade 40 units of food to Japan in exchange for 40 units of clothing. Both countries end up with more of both goods.

Outsourcing and Offshoring

People often confuse outsourcing and offshoring. Outsourcing is work done by another company or by people who are not employees of the original company. Offshoring is work done in another country.

Offshoring often benefits consumers. U.S. companies offshore work only if it costs less to do so. Companies offshore in order to lower costs and thus raise profits. If the cost to produce a good is lower, then the price of the good will fall. Consumers will end up paying lower prices. Offshoring is comparative advantage at work.

The Costs of Offshoring Are Easier to See than the Benefits

One cost of offshoring is that American workers lose their jobs when U.S. companies send work to foreign countries. But offshoring also has benefits. Foreign companies also offshore jobs to U.S. workers.

Another benefit is that lower prices may result from offshoring. Prices are often lower because U.S. companies can often lower their costs by offshoring.

The costs of offshoring are much easier to see than the benefits. For this reason, many people think that offshoring is only costs.

Answer questions 1–3 in the Section 1 Assessment on page 446 of your textbook.

CHAPTER 15, SECTION 2

Outlining Activity

Look through the chapter for an overview of the material. Pay attention to the main topics in the book. As you scan each section of the book, fill in the missing words in the following outline.

I. Trade Restrictions: Tariffs and Quotas

A. A(n) _____ is a tax on imports.

B. A(n) _____ is a legal limit on the amount of a good that may be imported.

C. _____ and _____ raise the price of imported goods for U.S. consumers.

II. The U.S. Government and Producer Interests

A. Government is sometimes more responsive to _____ interests than _____ interests.

B. _____ want to protect themselves from foreign competition so they _____ for tariffs.

C. The benefits of tariffs are _____ on relatively few producers, and the costs of tariffs are _____ relatively many consumers.

D. Each _____ gain is relatively large compared to each _____ loss.

E. _____ hear from the people who want _____ but not from the people who don't want them.

III. Tariffs and the Great Depression

A. In January 1929, many members of Congress became disturbed over the _____ in imports into the United States.

B. The _____ Act proposed substantially _____ tariffs on many imported goods. It was thought with _____ tariffs on imported goods, Americans would buy _____ imports and _____ goods produced in the United States.

C. Many economists today believe that the act not only served as one of the catalysts of the
_____ but also made the _____ last longer than it would
have otherwise.

IV. Arguments for Trade Restrictions

A. The _____ Argument

    1. People often argue that certain industries (aircraft, petroleum, chemicals, and weapons)
are necessary to the _____ and should be protected from foreign
competition.

    2. Critics say the argument may be overused or abused.

B. The _____ Argument

    1. Some people say that "_____" industries may need temporary protection
from more established foreign competitors until they are mature enough to compete on an
equal basis.

    2. Critics say that once an industry is protected from foreign competition, removing the
protection is almost impossible.

C. The _____ Argument

    1. Some people argue that a country may sell goods at prices below their
_____ and below the prices charged in the domestic market in
order to drive out domestic _____.

    2. Critics say a dumping strategy is not likely to work. Once the dumpers have driven out their
_____ and raised prices, their _____ is likely to
return. Also, U.S. _____ benefit from dumping by paying lower prices.

D. The _____ Argument

    1. Some people argue that American producers can't compete with foreign producers because
American producers pay _____ to their workers and foreign producers
pay _____ to their workers.

    2. This argument overlooks the fact that high wages and high productivity usually go together.

E. The _____ Argument

    1. Some people argue that if a foreign country uses tariffs or quotas against American goods,
then the United States should use tariffs and quotas against that foreign country in the hope
that the foreign country will lower or eliminate its _____.

2. Critics say that this type of policy has the potential to escalate into a full-blown

_____.

V. International Economic Integration

A. International economic integration occurs when nations combine to form either a

_____ market or a _____ area.

B. In a(n) _____ market, the member nations _____

without restrictions, and all share the same _____ with the outside world.

   1. A major common market is the _____ (EU). The EU consists of

      28 countries.

   2. The common currency in 19 of the 28 members of the EU is the _____.

C. In a(n) _____ area, trade barriers among the member countries are

_____. Each country is allowed to set its own trade rules with the rest of the

world.

   1. A major free trade area was created by the _____,

      and includes Canada, Mexico, and the United States.

   2. The _____ is a

      free trade agreement between the United States, Guatemala, Honduras, Nicaragua, and the

      Dominican Republic. It reduces barriers to trade between its member countries.

VI. International Organizations

A. Increasingly, countries of the world are finding it in their best interests to

_____ trade barriers between themselves and their neighbors.

B. The World Trade Organization provides a forum for member countries to discuss and

_____ trade issues. It also provides a system for adjudicating trade

_____.

C. The _____, officially known as the International Bank for Reconstruction

and Development, is the biggest development bank in the world. Its primary function is to

_____ to the world's poor and less-developed countries.

D. The _____ is an international organization that, among other

things, provides economic _____ and temporary funds for nations with

economic difficulties.

CHAPTER 15, SECTION 2

Just the Facts Handout

Trade Restrictions: Tariffs and Quotas

Tariffs and quotas are the two major types of trade restrictions. A **tariff** is a tax on imports. A quota is a legal limit on the amount of a good that may be imported. Both tariffs and quotas raise the prices of imported goods for U.S. consumers.

The U.S. Government and Producer Interests

Few producers gain the benefits from tariffs. In contrast, many consumers pay the costs of tariffs. This makes each producer's gain large compared with each consumer's loss.

For example, suppose that 100 producers sell good X, and 20 million consumers buy good X. If a tariff is placed on good X, the 100 producers will get a total of $40 million more. The 20 million consumers will pay a total of $40 million more. This means that each producer will get $400,000 more. Each consumer will pay $2 more. The benefit of the tariff is much greater for each producer than the loss is for each consumer.

Individual producers have a lot to gain from tariffs. Therefore, they are likely to lobby government for tariffs. However, individual consumers do lose much from tariffs. Therefore, they are not likely to lobby government against tariffs.

Thus, politicians hear from the producers who want tariffs. But politicians don't hear from the consumers who don't want tariffs. The politicians respond to the producers and impose tariffs.

Tariffs and the Great Depression

In 1929, many members of Congress were worried about the increase in imported goods. The Smoot-Hawley Tariff Act was proposed. This act would place much higher tariffs on many imported goods. Some people thought the higher tariffs would cause Americans to buy fewer imports and buy more goods produced in the United States. They thought this would be good for the country.

Other people disagreed. They thought the higher tariffs would be bad for business in the United States. They thought that other countries would retaliate with their own high tariffs. If this happened, global trade would lessen, thus hurting the U.S. economy.

Many economists today believe that the Smoot-Hawley Tariff Act was one of the things that led to the Great Depression. They also believe the act made the Great Depression last longer that it would have otherwise.

Arguments for Trade Restrictions

People have put forth various arguments in favor of tariffs and quotas.

The National-Defense Argument

People often argue that certain industries are necessary to the national defense. Examples of these industries are aircraft, oil, chemicals, and weapons. Such industries should be protected from foreign competition. The national-defense argument may be logical. However, it has been overused or abused in the past.

The Infant-Industry Argument

Some people argue that industries should be protected from foreign producers when they are new. This gives "infant" industries a chance to establish themselves and grow. However, once an industry is protected from foreign competition, removing the protection can be difficult.

The Antidumping Argument

Dumping is selling goods in foreign countries at prices below their costs and below the prices charged in domestic (home) markets. Some people argue that dumpers only want to get into a market, drive out U.S. competitors, and then raise prices. However, some economists point out that once the dumpers have done that, their competition is likely to return. These economists also point out that U.S. consumers benefit from dumping because they pay lower prices.

The Low-Foreign-Wages Argument

Some people argue that U.S. producers can't compete with foreign producers because of wages. They point out that U.S. producers pay high wages to their workers and foreign producers pay low wages. This argument overlooks one possible reason U.S. wages are higher than foreign wages. U.S. workers may be more productive than foreign workers. High wages and high productivity usually go together. Low wages and low productivity also go together.

The Tit-for-Tat Argument

Some people argue that if a foreign country uses tariffs or quotas against U.S. goods, then the United States should use tariffs or quotas against that foreign country. These people believe that the foreign country will then lower or its trade restrictions or get rid of them. Critics of this policy argue that a tit-for-tat strategy can grow into a trade war.

International Economic Integration

In a common market, the members trade without restrictions. These member nations all share the same trade barriers with the outside world. A major common market is the European Union (EU), which consists of 28 countries. Currently, the euro is a common currency in 19 of the 28 countries of the EU.

In a free trade area, trade barriers among the member countries are eliminated. Also, each country is allowed to set its own trade rules with the rest of the world. A major free trade area created by the North American Free Trade Agreement (NAFTA) includes Canada, Mexico, and the United States. In 2005, Congress passed the Central American-Dominican Republic Free Trade Agreement (CAFTA-DR). The CAFTA-DR countries are the United States, Costa Rica, El Salvador, Guatemala, Honduras, Nicaragua, and the Dominican Republic.

International Organizations

International organizations provide trade and economic help to countries. These organizations include the following:
- The World Trade Organization (WTO) provides a place for discussing and negotiating trade issues. It also provides a system for settling trade disputes.
- The World Bank is the biggest development bank in the world. Its official name is the International Bank for Reconstruction and Development (IBRD). Its main function is to lend money to poor and less-developed countries.
- The International Monetary Fund (IMF) helps nations with economic difficulties. It provides economic advice and temporary funds, among other things.

Answer questions 1–4 in the Section 2 Assessment on page 454 of your textbook.

CHAPTER 15, SECTION 3
Outlining Activity

Look through the chapter for an overview of the material. Pay attention to the main topics in the book. As you scan each section of the book, fill in the missing words in the following outline.

I. What Is an Exchange Rate?

A. The exchange rate is the _____ of one nation's currency in terms of another nation's currency.

B. In a(n) _____ exchange rate system, exchange rates are determined by the forces of supply and demand.

C. In a(n) _____ exchange rate system, exchange rates are determined by the government.

II. Appreciation and Depreciation

A. Depreciation is a(n) _____ in the value of one currency relative to other currencies. A currency has depreciated if it buys _____ of another currency.

B. Appreciation is a(n) _____ in the value of one currency relative to other currencies. A currency has appreciated if it buys _____ of another currency.

III. If the Dollar Depreciates, Foreign Goods Are _____ Expensive

A. When one's domestic currency depreciates, it becomes _____ expensive to buy foreign-produced goods.

B. For example, if the dollar depreciates, it's more expensive to buy foreign-produced goods.

```
Dollar depreciates → Foreign goods become more expensive
```

C. When one's domestic currency appreciates, it becomes _____ expensive to buy foreign-produced goods.

D. For example, if the dollar appreciates, it's cheaper to buy foreign-produced goods.

```
Dollar appreciates → Foreign goods become cheaper
```

CHAPTER 15, SECTION 3

Just the Facts Handout

What Is an Exchange Rate?

The **exchange rate** is the price of one country's currency in terms of another country's currency. The exchange rate is important when you travel.

Suppose you go to Italy. To buy goods and services in Italy, you will need the currency used in Italy. The basic unit of currency in Italy is the euro. Therefore, you will need to exchange your dollars for euros. Suppose you want to exchange $200 for euros. The number of euros you get for your $200 depends on the exchange rate.

The exchange rate may be determined in two different ways. Under a **flexible exchange rate system,** the forces of supply and demand determine the exchange rate. Under a **fixed exchange rate system,** countries' governments determine the exchange rate.

You can find out how much a foreign good costs in your money using three simple steps:

1. Find the current exchange rate. (Exchange rates are often listed in daily newspapers and online.)
2. Figure out how much of your money it takes to buy 1 unit of the foreign money.
3. Multiply the number of units in the price of the foreign good by your answer to step 2.

On your trip to Italy, suppose you see a jacket you want to buy. The price of the jacket is 100 euros. You want to know how much the jacket costs in dollars.

1. You find out the current exchange rate is 1 dollar = 0.80 euros.
2. You know from step 1 that 1 dollar = 0.80 euros, but you don't know what 1 euro equals in dollars. You can find out from the exchange rate as follows:

$$1 \text{ dollar} = 0.80 \text{ euros}$$
$$1 \text{ dollar} \div 0.80 = 0.80 \text{ euros} \div 0.80$$
$$1.25 \text{ dollars} = 1 \text{ euro}$$

3. The price of the jacket is 100 euros, so there are 100 units in the price of the foreign good. $1.25 \times 100 = \$125$.

So, the jacket costs $125.

Appreciation and Depreciation

Exchange rates can change from day to day. For example, on Monday, you may be able to get 0.80 euros for a dollar. But on Friday, you may be able to get only 0.75 euros for a dollar. **Depreciation** is a decrease in the value of one currency relative to other currencies. A currency has depreciated if it buys less of another currency.

Appreciation is the opposite of depreciation. **Appreciation** is an increase in the value of one currency relative to other currencies. A currency has appreciated if it buys more of another currency. For example, suppose the exchange rate goes from 1 dollar = 0.80 euros to 1 dollar = 0.90 euros. The dollar buys more euros, so the dollar has appreciated in value.

If the Dollar Depreciates, Foreign Goods Are More Expensive

When one's domestic currency depreciates, it becomes more expensive to buy foreign-produced goods. So when the dollar depreciates, foreign goods become more expensive. Americans must pay more dollars to buy foreign-produced goods.

When one's domestic currency appreciates, it becomes cheaper to buy foreign-produced goods. So when the dollar appreciates, foreign goods become cheaper. Americans pay fewer dollars to buy foreign-produced goods.

Answer questions 1–3 in the Section 3 Assessment on page 459 of your textbook.

Name: _____ Date: _____

CHAPTER 15, SECTION 4

Outlining Activity

Look through the chapter for an overview of the material. Pay attention to the main topics in the book. As you scan each section of the book, fill in the missing words in the following outline.

I. How Countries Are Classified

    A. A(n) _____ country has a relatively _____ per capita GDP.

    B. A(n) _____ country has a relatively _____ per capita GDP.

    C. For example, the United States is a _____ country, and Ethiopia is a _____ country.

II. Obstacles to Economic Development

    A. Rapid _____

        1. _____ growth rates are usually _____ in less-developed countries than in developed countries.

> Population growth rate = Birthrate − Death rate

        2. The _____ tends to be higher in less-developed nations. In countries where pensions and social security do not exist and where the economy revolves around agriculture, children are often seen as essential _____ and as _____ for parents in their old age.

        3. In the past few decades, the _____ has fallen in less-developed countries, largely because of medical advances.

        4. The combination of higher _____ and declining _____ means population grows more rapidly in less-developed countries than in developed countries.

    B. Low _____ Rate

        1. Some economists argue that the less-developed countries have low _____ rates because the people living there are so poor that they can't save.

Guided Reading and Study Guide © EMC Publishing

2. This creates a vicious _____. Less-developed countries are poor because they can't save and buy _____ goods, but they can't save and buy _____ goods because they are poor.

3. Other economists argue that being poor is not a _____ to economic development. They say that many nations that are rich today were poor in the past but still managed to become economically developed.

C. Cultural Differences

   1. Some cultures are reluctant to depart from the _____ (existing state of affairs). They view change as dangerous and risky.

   2. In some cultures, people are _____ by Western standards. They believe that a person's good or bad fortune in life depends more on _____ or the _____ than on how hard the person works, or how much he or she learns, or how hard he or she strives to succeed.

D. Political _____ and Government _____ of Private Property

E. High _____ Rates

III. Factors That _____ Growth and Development

A. Free Trade

   1. Free trade lets _____ of a country buy inputs from the cheapest supplier, no matter where in the world it is located.

   2. Free trade opens up a world market to _____ firms.

B. Low Taxation

   1. _____ provide a greater incentive to workers to work and investors to invest than exists in a country with relatively high taxes.

C. Absence of _____ on Foreign Investment

D. Absence of _____ on Bank _____ Activity

E. Absence of _____ and _____ Controls

F. Simple, Easy Business _____ Procedures

G. Protecting _____ Property

H. Incentives

CHAPTER 15, SECTION 4

Just the Facts Handout

How Countries Are Classified

A **developed country** is a country that has a relatively high per capita GDP. A **less-developed country** is a country that has a relatively low per capita GDP. The United States is a developed country. Haiti is a less-developed country.

Obstacles to Economic Development

Some factors help to determine why some countries are poor while others are rich.

Rapid Population Growth

The population growth rate is often higher in less-developed countries than in developed countries. The **population growth rate** is equal to the birthrate minus the death rate. For example, suppose in a given year, the birthrate in a country is 3 percent and the death rate is 2 percent. Then the population growth rate in the country is 1 percent.

The relatively high population growth rate in less-developed countries has two causes. First, the birthrate tends to be higher than the birthrate of developed nations. People tend to have more children because pensions and social security do not exist and the economy is based on agriculture. Children are seen as essential labor and as security for parents in their old age. Second, the death rate has fallen in less-developed countries due to medical advances.

The combination of higher birthrates and falling death rates explains why the population grows more rapidly in less-developed countries than in developed countries.

A rapid population growth rate is not always an obstacle to economic development. Many of the developed countries today had faster population growth rates when they were developing than the less-developed countries have today.

Low Savings Rate

Some economists argue that the less-developed countries have low savings rates because the people are so poor that they cannot save. This situation is called the vicious circle of poverty. Less-developed countries are poor because they cannot save and buy capital goods, but they cannot save and buy capital goods because they are poor.

Other economists argue that being poor is not a barrier to economic development. They say that many nations that are rich today, such as the United States, were poor in the past. These countries still managed to become economically developed.

Cultural Differences

The culture in some less-developed countries may hinder economic growth and development. For example, some cultures are reluctant to depart from the status quo (the existing state of affairs). People view change as dangerous and risky.

Also in some cultures, the people are fatalistic by Western standards. They believe that a person's fortune in life depends on fate or the spirits. They believe that it doesn't matter how hard people work, how much they learn, or how hard they try to succeed.

Political Instability and Government Seizure of Private Property

Individuals sometimes don't invest money in businesses in less-developed countries because it's risky to do so. The current government leaders could be thrown out of office or the government could seize their private property.

High Tax Rates

Some economists argue that high tax rates hinder economic development.

Factors That Aid Growth and Development

Some economists believe that certain factors can help poor countries become rich countries.

Free Trade

Countries can hinder or promote free trade. They promote it by eliminating tariffs, quotas, and anything else that prevents the free flow of resources and goods between countries. Free trade promotes the production of goods and services in a country. It encourages growth and development in two ways. First, free trade allows residents of a country to buy inputs from the cheapest supplier. Second, free trade opens up a world market to domestic firms.

Low Taxation

Generally, low taxes provide an incentive to workers to work and to investors to invest. Both of these activities encourage economic growth.

Absence of Restrictions on Foreign Investment

Some countries prevent foreigners from investing in their countries. Such restrictions often hamper economic growth and development. Allowing foreigners to invest in a country, to start or expand businesses, promotes growth and development.

Absence of Controls on Bank Lending Activity

Banks channel funds from those who save to those who want to invest and produce. In some countries, government tells banks to whom they can and cannot lend. Controls of this type often hinder growth and development.

Absence of Wage and Price Controls

The free market determines equilibrium prices and wages. When government "overrides" the market and places controls on prices and wages, production usually suffers. Price and wage controls raise production costs, making it likely that firms will go out of business. The goods and services these firms once produced will no longer exist.

Simple, Easy Business Licensing Procedures

Most countries require a person to have a business license before starting a business. The easier and cheaper it is to obtain a business license, the more new businesses pop up. New businesses often promote economic growth and development.

Protecting Private Property

People will not work hard or invest in businesses unless they are reasonably sure that the government will not take their property. Countries that protect private property often develop faster than those that do not.

Incentives

The incentive structure in a country appears to be a factor in motivation.

Answer questions 1–3 in the Section 4 Assessment on page 465 of your textbook.

CHAPTER 15

Graphic Organizer Activity

Supply the missing words in the blank spaces of these graphic organizers.

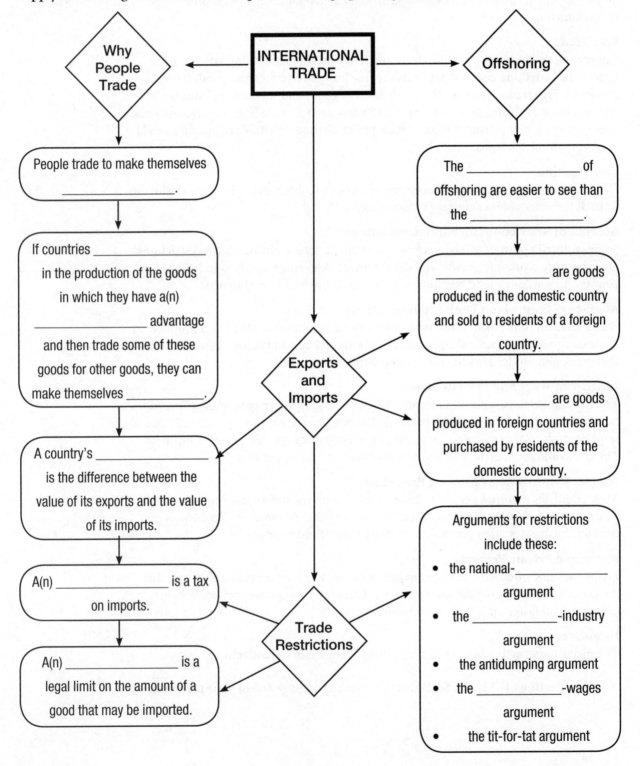

Why People Trade

People trade to make themselves _____.

If countries _____ in the production of the goods in which they have a(n) _____ advantage and then trade some of these goods for other goods, they can make themselves _____.

A country's _____ is the difference between the value of its exports and the value of its imports.

A(n) _____ is a tax on imports.

A(n) _____ is a legal limit on the amount of a good that may be imported.

INTERNATIONAL TRADE

Exports and Imports

Trade Restrictions

Offshoring

The _____ of offshoring are easier to see than the _____.

_____ are goods produced in the domestic country and sold to residents of a foreign country.

_____ are goods produced in foreign countries and purchased by residents of the domestic country.

Arguments for restrictions include these:
- the national-_____ argument
- the _____-industry argument
- the antidumping argument
- the _____-wages argument
- the tit-for-tat argument

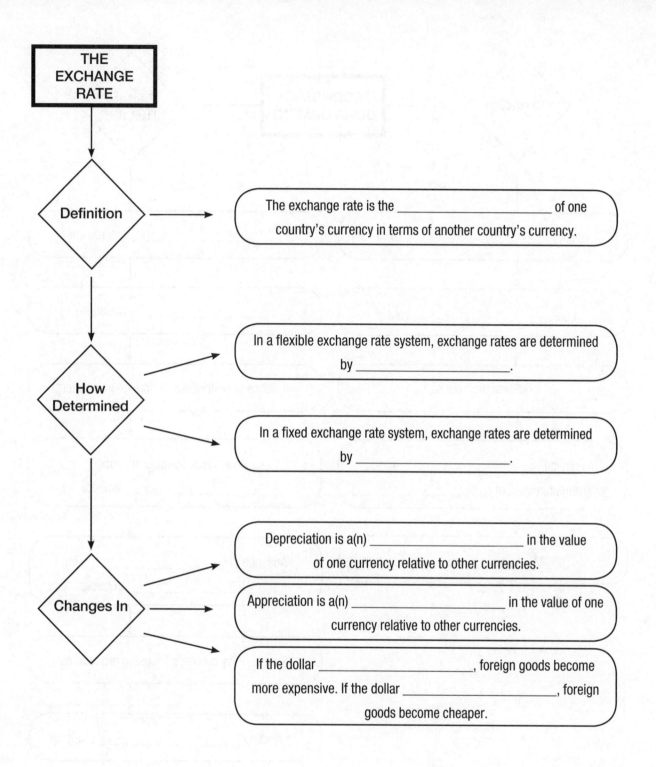

THE EXCHANGE RATE

Definition

The exchange rate is the _____ of one country's currency in terms of another country's currency.

How Determined

In a flexible exchange rate system, exchange rates are determined by _____.

In a fixed exchange rate system, exchange rates are determined by _____.

Changes In

Depreciation is a(n) _____ in the value of one currency relative to other currencies.

Appreciation is a(n) _____ in the value of one currency relative to other currencies.

If the dollar _____, foreign goods become more expensive. If the dollar _____, foreign goods become cheaper.

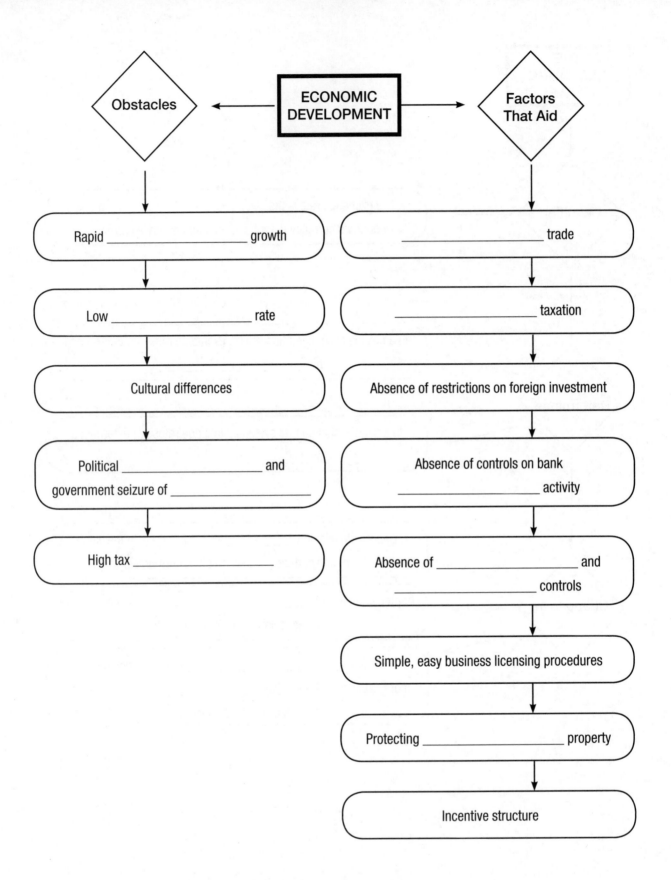

ECONOMIC DEVELOPMENT

Obstacles

Rapid _____ growth

Low _____ rate

Cultural differences

Political _____ and government seizure of _____

High tax _____

Factors That Aid

_____ trade

_____ taxation

Absence of restrictions on foreign investment

Absence of controls on bank _____ activity

Absence of _____ and _____ controls

Simple, easy business licensing procedures

Protecting _____ property

Incentive structure

CHAPTER 15

Vocabulary Activity

For each question, fill in the blank with the correct term from the following list.

exports	outsourcing	depreciation
imports	tariff	appreciation
balance of trade	dumping	developed country
absolute advantage	exchange rate	less-developed country
specialize	flexible exchange rate system	population growth rate
comparative advantage	fixed exchange rate system	

1. The price of one country's currency in terms of another country's currency is the

   _____.

2. To _____ is to do only one thing.

3. A tax on imports is a(n) _____.

4. _____ are goods produced in the domestic country and sold to residents of a

   foreign country.

5. Under a(n) _____, currency exchange rates are determined by the forces

   of supply and demand.

6. _____ is the situation in which a country can produce more of a good than

   another country can produce with the same quantity of resources.

7. _____ describes work done for a company by another company or by people

   other than the original company's employees.

8. The sale of goods abroad at prices below their costs and below the price charged in domestic (home)

   markets is _____.

9. _____ is an increase in the value of one currency relative to other currencies.

10. _____ is the situation in which a country can produce a good at lower opportunity

    cost than another country.

11. A(n) _____ is a country with a relatively low per capita GDP.

12. _____ are goods produced in foreign countries and purchased by residents of the

    domestic country.

13. Under a(n) _____, currency exchange rates are fixed, or pegged, by countries' governments.

14. The _____ is the birthrate minus the death rate.

15. The difference between the value of a country's exports and the value of its imports is its _____.

16. _____ is a decrease in the value of one currency relative to other currencies.

17. A(n) _____ is a country with a relatively high per capita GDP.

CHAPTER 15

Working with Graphs and Tables Activity

You are planning a vacation to Mexico. You have purchased your airline ticket and have budgeted $500 for hotel rooms, meals, and spending money while in Mexico. You also want to buy some pottery. You know that the style of pottery you want costs 50 pesos. One week before you are due to leave, the exchange rate is 1 dollar = 2 pesos. Then the day you leave, you find out that the exchange rate is now 1 dollar = 5 pesos. Complete the table and then answer the questions.

	Exchange rate: 1 dollar = 2 pesos	Exchange rate: 1 dollar = 5 pesos
Number of pesos in $500		
Cost of pottery in dollars		

1. On the day you leave for Mexico, what has happened to the dollar? What has happened to the peso?

   _____

   _____

2. Overall, how has the change in the exchange rate affected your vacation?

   _____

   _____

3. Will the new exchange rate affect how many people from the United States visit Mexico? Why?

   _____

   _____

CHAPTER 15

Practice Test

Multiple Choice

Circle the letter of the correct answer.

1. What is the price of one country's currency in terms of another country's currency called?

    a. the depreciation rate
    b. the comparative advantage
    c. the fixed rate
    d. the exchange rate

2. The exchange rate is 1 dollar = 0.23 British pounds and the price of an American good is 435

    dollars. What is the price in British pounds?

    a. 123. 03 pounds
    b. 100.05 pounds
    c. 101.00 pounds
    d. 99.30 pounds

3. Which of the following is a tax that a country places on imports?

    a. quota
    b. tariff
    c. depreciation
    d. comparative disadvantage

4. Which of the following is a legal limit on the amount of a good that may be imported?

    a. quota
    b. tariff
    c. depreciation
    d. comparative disadvantage

5. If the value of a country's exports exceeds the value of its imports, then the country has which of the

    following?

    a. trade surplus
    b. trade deficit
    c. absolute advantage
    d. comparative advantage

6. If the value of a country's exports is less than the value of its imports, then the country has which of

    the following?

    a. trade surplus
    b. trade deficit
    c. absolute advantage
    d. comparative advantage

7. Canada can produce lumber at a lower opportunity cost than Japan can produce lumber. Then Canada has which of the following?

   a. an absolute advantage in the production of lumber
   b. a comparative advantage in the production of lumber
   c. lower appreciation in the production of lumber
   d. an absolute benefit in the production of lumber

8. A country that sells its goods in other countries at prices below their costs and below the price charged in domestic markets is doing which of the following?

   a. exporting
   b. importing
   c. tariffing
   d. dumping

9. Which of the following is an increase in the value of one currency relative to other currencies?

   a. comparative advantage
   b. absolute advantage
   c. appreciation
   d. depreciation

10. In one year, the value of U.S. exports was $150 billion and the value of U.S. imports was $129 billion. What was the balance of trade for the United States that year?

   a. $21 billion
   b. –$21 billion
   c. $279 billion
   d. –$279 billion

True or False

For each of these statements, place a *T* in the blank if the statement is true or an *F* if the statement is false.

1. _____ A tariff restricts the amount of foreign goods that can be imported into a country.

2. _____ A comparative advantage in the production of skateboards means a country is the low opportunity cost producer of skateboards.

3. _____ The low-foreign-wages argument states that U.S. producers cannot compete with companies in other countries that pay higher wages.

4. _____ The critics of the low-foreign-wages argument say that producers care about more than wages; they care about productivity, too.

5. _____ Under a flexible exchange rate system, a decrease in the demand for Japanese yen will increase the price of a yen.

6. _____ If a country's population growth rate is 2 percent and its birthrate is 5 percent, then its death rate is 3 percent.

Short Answer

Write your answers on the lines provided.

1. After a quota is imposed on imported cars, would you expect consumers to buy more or fewer imported cars, all other things remaining the same? Explain your answer.

   _____

   _____

2. Would U.S. producers of cars favor a quota on imported cars?

   _____

   _____

   _____

3. If tariffs and quotas hurt domestic consumers, then why does the government impose them?

   _____

   _____

   _____

   _____

4. What are some reasons that people in less-developed countries have more children than people in developed countries?

   _____

   _____

   _____

CHAPTER 16, SECTION 1
Outlining Activity

Look through the chapter for an overview of the material. Pay attention to the main topics in the book. As you scan each section of the book, fill in the missing words in the following outline.

I. Financial Markets

    A. Buying and selling stocks and bonds occurs in a(n) _____ market.

    B. Financial markets allow a person either to _____ in a company or to lend the company some money.

    C. For example, Jones might buy _____ in a company or he might buy a _____ that a company is issuing.

II. What Are Stocks?

    A. An owner of a company's stock is a part owner of the _____.

    B. A stock is a claim on the _____ of a corporation that gives the purchaser a share of the corporation.

III. Where Is Stock Bought and Sold?

    A. People buy and sell stock at the _____ (NYSE).

    B. The _____ stock market is a(n) _____ stock market with trades executed through a computer and telecommunications network.

IV. The _____ Industrial Average (DJIA)

    A. The DJIA is a widely cited indicator of _____ stock market activity. It is a weighted average of _____.

    B. Other prominent stock indices are the _____ Composite, the _____ 500, the _____ 2000, and the _____ 5000.

    C. According to many economists, the _____ is closely connected to changes in such things as consumer credit, business expectations, exports and imports, personal income, and the money supply.

V. How the Stock Market Works

A. A company can raise money in three ways. It can _____ money from a bank. It can borrow money by issuing a(n) _____. It can sell or issue _____ in the company.

B. When a company issues or sells stock (also called _____), it sells part of the company.

C. When a company is initially formed, the owners set up a certain amount of stock, which is worth very little money.

D. As the company grows and needs more money, it may decide to offer its stock on the _____ market.

E. The company makes a(n) _____ (IPO) of its stock. Usually a(n) _____ bank sells the stock for the company.

F. After an IPO of a stock, the stock is usually traded on an exchange or in an electronic stock market.

G. The _____ of a stock depends on the forces of supply and demand.

H. People buy a particular stock if they think that the _____ of the company that initially issued the stock are likely to _____.

VI. Why Do People Buy and Sell Stock?

A. Some people buy stock for the _____. _____ are payments made to _____ based on a company's profits.

B. People also buy stocks because they think the stock's _____ will rise.

VII. How to Buy and Sell Stock

A. You can buy or sell stock through a(n) _____ stock brokerage firm, a(n) _____ broker, or a(n) _____ broker.

B. With a(n) _____ broker, you may call up on the phone and ask your broker to recommend some good stock.

C. A(n) _____ broker simply executes a trade for you and does not offer any advice.

D. In _____ trading, you go to your broker's website, log in by entering your username and password, and then buy or sell stock.

VIII. Deciding Which Stocks to Buy

A. One way to buy stocks is to simply buy shares of stock that you think are going to

_____ in price.

B. Another way to buy stocks is to invest in a stock mutual fund.

1. A stock mutual fund is a(n) _____ of stocks. A fund manager who works

for a mutual fund company manages the fund.

2. If you put money in a mutual fund, you are in effect buying the stocks in that fund.

3. The fund manager _____ which stocks will be bought and sold.

C. A third way to buy stocks is to buy the stocks that make up a(n) _____ like

the DJIA, Standard & Poor's 500, or Wilshire 5000.

1. Spyders, or SPDRs, which stands for "Standard & Poor's Depository Receipts," are

securities in the SPDR Trust. The SPDR Trust buys the stocks that make up the

_____ 500 index.

2. When you buy Spyders, you are buying the stock of 500 companies. This is sometimes called

"_____."

IX. How to Read the Stock Market Page

A. 52W high is the _____ of the stock during the past year or past 52 weeks.

B. 52W low is the _____ of the stock during the past 52 weeks.

C. A stock is listed using either a(n) _____ of the name of the company or the

full name of the company.

D. A(n) _____ is shown for a company's stock.

E. _____ is the last annual dividend per share of stock.

F. Yield% is the _____ divided by the _____ price.

$$\text{Yield} = \frac{\text{Dividend per share}}{\text{Closing price per share}}$$

G. P/E is the PE ratio, or _____ ratio. A(n) _____ PE ratio

usually indicates that people believe there will be higher than average growth in earnings.

$$\text{PE} = \frac{\text{Closing price per share}}{\text{Net earnings per share}}$$

H. _____ is the volume of shares traded in the hundreds on the current day.

I. _____ is the high price the stock traded for on the current day.

J. _____ is the low price the stock traded for on the current day.

K. _____ is the share price of the stock when trading stopped on the current day.

L. Net chg is the _____, the difference between the current day's closing price and the previous day's closing price.

CHAPTER 16, SECTION 1

Just the Facts Handout

Financial Markets

Stocks are bought and sold in a financial market. Financial markets bring together two groups of people: (1) people who want to invest money and (2) people who have companies that need money.

What Are Stocks?

A **stock** is a claim on the assets of a corporation that gives the purchaser a share in the corporation.

Where Is Stock Bought and Sold?

Every weekday, people meet at the New York Stock Exchange (NYSE) and buy and sell stock. If you want to buy or sell a stock, you simply contact a stock broker. The broker tells a person at the NYSE what you want to do. The person at the NYSE buys or sells the stock.

The NYSE is not the only place where stocks are bought and sold. Other stock exchanges exist, including the National Association of Securities Dealers Automated Quotations (NASDAQ) stock market. The NASDAQ is an electronic stock market. Instead of meeting in person, traders use a computer and telecommunications network.

The Dow Jones Industrial Average (DJIA)

The **Dow Jones Industrial Average (DJIA)** is the most popular indicator of what happens in the stock market from one day to the next. It gives people an idea of whether stock prices in general are rising or falling.

The DJIA consists of the stocks of 30 companies. (See Exhibit 16-1 on page 472 of your textbook.) The DJIA is not a simple average. In other words, it is not computed by simply adding up the prices of the stocks and dividing by 30. Instead, the prices of the stocks are summed and are then divided by a special number. This special divisor is used so that price changes in one or two stocks do not give a false impression of the market as a whole.

The DJIA is not the only stock index. Other well-known stock indices are the NASDAQ Composite, the Standard & Poor's 500, the Russell 2000, and the Wilshire 5000.

Many economists say that the DJIA is closely connected to changes in such things as consumer credit, business expectations, exports and imports, personal income, and the money supply. For example, suppose consumer credit rises. This rise indicates that people are buying more goods and services. That is good for the companies that sell the goods and services. So we would expect the DJIA to rise if consumer credit rises.

How the Stock Market Works

A company can raise money in three ways:

1. It can go to a bank and borrow money.
2. It can borrow money by issuing a bond. (A bond is a promise to repay the borrowed money with interest.)
3. It can sell or issue stock in the company.

When a company is started, the owners set up a certain amount of stock. The owners try to find people, often friends and relatives, who are willing to buy the stock. These people hope that the company will be successful someday.

If the company grows, it will likely need more money. When the company needs more money, the owners may decide to offer the company's stock on the open market. To do this, the company makes an **initial public offering (IPO)** of the stock. Usually an **investment bank** sells the stock for the company for an initial price, such as $10 a share.

What happens to the price of the stock after the IPO? The outcome depends on the forces of supply and demand. If demand rises and supply is constant, then the price of the stock will rise. If demand falls and supply is constant, then the price of the stock will fall.

Demand will rise if people think that the earnings of the company are likely to rise. The more profitable a company is expected to be, the more likely people are going to want to own the company. And if people want to own the company, the demand for the company's stock will rise.

Why Do People Buy and Sell Stock?

Some people buy stocks for the dividends. **Dividends** are payments made to stockholders based on a company's profits. For example, suppose you own 500 shares of a stock and the company decides to pay a yearly dividend of $1 per share. You receive a check for $500.

The other reason people buy stock is because they think the price of the stock will rise. People can make money if they sell their stock at a price that's higher than the price they paid. For example, you might buy stock for $1 a share today if you think that the price will be $3 a share next year.

How to Buy and Sell Stock

Buying and selling stock is called executing a trade. You can buy or sell stock through a full-service stock brokerage firm, a discount broker, or an online broker. Full-service brokers will recommend stocks for you in addition to executing trades. Discount and online brokers simply execute trades; they do not offer any advice.

Deciding Which Stocks to Buy

You can use various methods to decide which stocks to buy. You can simply buy stock that you think is going to rise in price, you can buy mutual funds, or you can "buy the market."

A stock mutual fund is a collection of stocks. A mutual fund company hires a fund manager to decide what stocks to buy and sell for the fund. You might invest in a stock mutual fund if you think the fund manager knows more than you do about how and when to buy and sell stocks.

"Buying the market" means buying shares in a fund that includes all the stock in a stock index. An **index** is a portfolio of stocks, which represent a particular market or a portion of it, used to measure changes in a market or an economy. The DJIA, the Standard & Poor's 500, and the Wilshire 5000 are stock indices.

For example, the SPDR Trust buys the stocks of the companies that make up the Standard & Poor's (S&P) 500 index. The SPDR Trust securities are called "Spyders." Spyders sell for a specific price, such as $120 a Spyder. You buy Spyders the same way you buy shares of stock. However, when you buy Spyders, you are actually buying the stock of 500 companies. Because you are buying the stock of so many companies, you are said to be "buying the market."

How to Read the Stock Market Page

The stock market page in the newspaper shows information about stocks. (See Exhibit 16-4 on page 481 of your textbook.) The columns of the stock market listing provide the following information for each stock:

- **52W High** is the high price of the stock during the past year or past 52 weeks.
- **52W Low** is the low price of the stock during the past 52 weeks.
- **Stock** is either an abbreviation or the full name of the company.
- **Ticker** is the stock or ticker symbol for the company.
- **Div** is the last annual dividend paid per share of stock.
- **Yield %** is the dividend divided by the closing price. A higher yield is better, all other things being the same.
- **P/E** is the price-earnings ratio. The PE ratio is the latest closing price per share divided by the latest available net earnings per share. For example, if a stock has a PE ratio of 14.5, the stock is selling for a share price that is 14.5 times its earnings per share.
- **Vol 00s** is the volume in hundreds. In other words, 6412 means that 641,200 shares of this stock were traded on the current day.
- **High** is the highest price the stock traded for on the current day.
- **Low** is the lowest price the stock traded for on the current day.
- **Close** is the share price of the stock when trading stopped on the current day.
- **Net chg** (net change) is the difference between the current closing price and the previous day's closing price.

Answer questions 1–4 in the Section 1 Assessment on page 481 of your textbook.

CHAPTER 16, SECTION 2

Outlining Activity

Look through the chapter for an overview of the material. Pay attention to the main topics in the book. As you scan each section of the book, fill in the missing words in the following outline.

I. What Is a Bond?

    A. A bond is a(n) _____, or a promise to pay.

    B. Companies, governments, and government agencies issue bonds for the purpose of borrowing money.

II. The Components of a Bond

    A. The face value, or _____, of a bond is the total amount the issuer of the bond will repay to the buyer of the bond.

    B. The _____ is the day when the issuer of the bond must pay the buyer of the bond the face value of the bond.

    C. The _____ is the percentage of the face value that the bondholder receives each year until the bond matures.

III. Bond Ratings

    A. The more likely the bond issuer will pay the face value of the bond at maturity and will meet all scheduled coupon payments, the _____ the bond's rating.

    B. Two of the best known ratings are _____ and _____.

    C. A bond rating of _____ from Standard & Poor's or a rating of _____ from Moody's is the highest possible rating. Such a bond would be one of the most secure bonds you can buy.

IV. Bond Prices and Yields

    A. The _____ of a bond may be equal to, less than, or greater than the face value of the bond.

    B. The greater the _____ for the bond relative to the _____, the higher the price.

C. The _____ on a bond is the coupon payment divided by the price paid for the bond.

$$\text{Yield} = \frac{\text{Annual coupon payment}}{\text{Price paid for the bond}}$$

D. As the price paid for a bond _____, the yield _____.

V. Types of Bonds

A. A(n) _____ bond is issued by a private corporation.

B. _____ bonds are issued by state and local governments.

C. The _____ issues Treasury bills (T-bills), notes, and bonds. The only difference between bills, notes, and bonds is their _____. Treasury bills mature in 13, 26, or 52 weeks. Treasury notes mature in 2 to 10 years, and Treasury bonds mature in 10 to 30 years.

D. A(n) _____ Treasury bond guarantees the purchaser a certain real rate of return.

VI. How to Read the Bond Market Page

A. Corporate Bonds

1. A bond is listed by a(n) _____ for the company that issued the bond and includes the coupon rate and the year the bond matures.

2. Cur. Yld. stands for _____.

3. _____ stands for volume of sales in dollars.

4. Close is the _____ price on this day.

5. _____ stands for net change.

B. Treasury Bonds

1. Rate is the _____ rate of the bond.

2. Maturity is the date the bond matures.

3. _____ is how much the buyer is willing to pay for the bond.

4. _____ is how much the seller is asking for the bond.

5. Chg is the _____ in the price of the bond from the previous trading day.

6. Yield is the _____ a person who buys the bond today (at the ask price) and holds it to _____ will realize.

VII. Risk and Return

A. People buy stocks and bonds for the _____.

B. Stocks and bonds come with different _____ and _____ factors. Buying stock in a new company might be _____ than buying a Treasury bond.

C. Higher returns come with higher _____ and lower returns come with lower _____.

VIII. What Would Life Be Like Without Financial Markets?

A. Without financial markets, you couldn't sell _____ in your new company and you couldn't issue _____ to borrow funds.

B. With financial markets, the people with good ideas can be _____ with the people who would like to invest.

C. _____ ends up with _____ goods and services because financial markets exist.

CHAPTER 16, SECTION 2

Just the Facts Handout

What Is a Bond?

A **bond** is an IOU, or a promise to pay. Companies, governments, and government agencies issue bonds in order to borrow money. The issuer of a bond is a borrower. The person who buys the bond is a lender.

The Components of a Bond

The **face value** of a bond is the dollar amount specified on the bond. This is also called the **par value** of a bond. It is the total amount the issuer of the bond will repay to the buyer of the bond. For example, suppose Dawson buys a bond from company Z. The face value of the bond is $10,000. Thus, company Z promises to pay Dawson $10,000 at some future time.

The maturity date is the day when the issuer of the bond must pay the buyer of the bond the face value of the bond. For example, suppose the maturity date of Dawson's $10,000 bond is December 31, 2020. On that date, Dawson will receive $10,000 from company Z.

The **coupon rate** is the percentage of the face value that the bondholder receives each year until the bond matures. For example, suppose Dawson's $10,000 bond has a coupon rate of 7 percent. Then Dawson will receive $10,000 \times 0.07 = $700 a year until the bond matures.

Bond Ratings

Bonds are rated or evaluated. The highest possible rating for a bond is AAA from Standard & Poor's or Aaa from Moody's. A bond with this rating is one of the most secure bonds you can buy. The bond issuer is almost certain to pay the face value of the bond at maturity. The issuer is also almost certain to meet all scheduled coupon payments.

Bond Prices and Yields

The price that a person pays for a bond depends on market conditions. The greater the demand for the bond relative to the supply, the higher the price. The price determines the yield that the bondholder receives on the bond. The **yield** is the annual coupon payment divided by the price paid for the bond. As the price paid for a bond rises, the yield declines.

For example, suppose Joshua buys a bond with a face value of $1,000 and a coupon rate of 5 percent. The coupon payment will be $50 (5 percent of $1,000). Consider three cases.

1. Joshua pays $950 for the bond. The yield will be $50 \div $950 = 5.26 percent.
2. Joshua pays $1,000 for the bond. The yield will be $50 \div $1,000 = 5 percent.
3. Joshua pays $1,100 for the bond. The yield will be $50 \div $1,100 = 4.54 percent.

The coupon payment stays the same in each case because it's based on the face value of the bond. But the yield declines as the price Joshua pays for the bond rises.

Types of Bonds

A corporate bond is issued by a private corporation. Corporate bonds may sell for a price above or below face value. The price depends on current supply and demand conditions for the bond.

Municipal bonds are issued by state and local governments. Municipal bonds are used to pay for such projects as roads and new sports stadiums. Many people buy municipal bonds because they don't have to pay federal taxes on the interest they receive on the bonds.

The federal government issues Treasury bills (T-bills), notes, and bonds. The difference between bills, notes, and bonds is their time to maturity. Treasury bills mature in the shortest time. Treasury bonds mature in the longest time. Treasury bills, notes, and bonds are considered safe investments. The federal government is unlikely to default on its bond obligations.

In 1997, the federal government began to issue inflation-indexed bonds. An inflation-indexed Treasury bond guarantees the purchaser a certain real rate of return, but a nonindexed Treasury bond does not. For example, if the inflation rate is 3 percent, the government will "mark up" the dollar amount of an inflation-indexed bond by 3 percent. Then the coupon payment will be based on this higher dollar amount.

How to Read the Bond Market Page

The bond market page of a newspaper gives information about different types of bonds. The information about corporate bonds is usually not the same as the information about Treasury bonds. (See page 487 of your textbook.)

The listing for corporate bonds includes (1) the name of the company issuing the bond, the coupon rate, and the maturity date; (2) the current yield; (3) the volume of sales in dollars; (4) the closing price; and (5) the change in price from the previous day.

The listing for Treasury bonds includes (1) the coupon rate; (2) the maturity date; (3) the price the buyer is willing to pay for the bond; (4) the price the seller is asking for the bond; (5) the change in price from the previous day; and (6) the yield if the bond is purchased at the asking price and held until maturity.

Risk and Return

Stocks and bonds often have different risks and returns. In general, higher returns have higher risks and lower returns have lower risks. For example, buying stock in a new company is likely to be riskier than buying a Treasury bond. You can be fairly sure that the U.S. Treasury is going to pay off its bond. However, you can't be so sure you'll have a positive return on the stock you buy in a new company.

What Would Life Be Like Without Financial Markets?

To understand the importance of financial markets, you need to imagine what the world would be like without them. Suppose that you have a great idea for a new product. Saving enough money to develop, produce, and sell the new product is almost impossible. In a world without financial markets, you have nowhere to turn. You can't sell stock in your new company because the stock market doesn't exist. You can't borrow money by issuing bonds because the bond market doesn't exist. Society never gets your new product.

In a world of financial markets, though, people with good ideas can be matched up with people who want to invest. As a result, society ends up with more goods and services than otherwise would be the case.

Answer questions 1–4 in the Section 2 Assessment on page 489 of your textbook.

CHAPTER 16, SECTION 3
Outlining Activity

Look through the chapter for an overview of the material. Pay attention to the main topics in the book. As you scan each section of the book, fill in the missing words in the following outline.

I. Futures

    A. A(n) _____ contract is an agreement to buy or sell a specific amount of something at a particular price on a stipulated future date.

    B. Myers, a miller, enters into the futures contract because he wants the peace of mind of knowing he will be able to buy wheat at a price that will let him earn a(n) _____ .

    C. Smith, a(n) _____ , enters into the futures contract because she hopes to earn a(n) _____ .

II. Currency Futures

    A. A(n) _____ futures contract is an agreement to buy or sell a specific amount of currency at a particular price on a stipulated future date.

    B. For example, suppose Bill needs a specific amount of yen at a(n) _____ date and wants to pay a specific amount of dollars for the yen. Julie agrees to sell Bill the yen at the future date for the price Bill wants to pay. Julie thinks that she will be able to make a(n) _____ by buying the yen for less than the price Bill has agreed to pay.

III. Options

    A. A(n) _____ is a contract that gives the owner the right, but not the obligation, to buy or sell shares of a stock at a specified price on or before a future date.

    B. A(n) _____ option gives the owner the right to buy shares of a stock at a specified price (strike price) within the time limits of the contract.

    C. A(n) _____ option gives the owner the right, but not the obligation, to sell shares of a stock at a strike price during some period of time.

IV. How You Can Use Call and Put Options

    A. If you think the price of a stock is going to rise, you would buy a call option.

    B. If you think the price of a stock is going to fall, you would buy a put option.

CHAPTER 16, SECTION 3

Just the Facts Handout

Futures

A **futures contract** is an agreement to buy or sell a specific amount of something at a particular price on a stipulated date in the future. For example, suppose Myers, a miller, has promised to deliver 1,000 pounds of flour to a baker in six months. Myers will need 200 bushels of wheat to make the 1,000 pounds of flour. Myers can make a profit on his sale of flour to the baker if he pays no more than $3 a bushel for the wheat. The price of wheat is $3 a bushel now. Myers doesn't know what the price will be in six months. Myers would like to be sure he can buy the wheat in six months for the $3 a bushel price.

Smith, a speculator, believes that the price of wheat will be less than $3 a bushel in six months. She believes that in six months, she will be able to buy 200 bushels of wheat for only $2 a bushel.

Myers and Smith enter into a futures contract. They agree that Smith will sell 200 bushels of wheat to Myers in six months for a price of $3 a bushel. With the futures contract, Myers knows that he will be able to buy the wheat he needs at a price that will let him earn a profit. With the futures contract, Smith takes a risk because the price of wheat might be more than $3 a bushel. But if she's right and the price is only $2 a bushel, then she earns a profit of $1 a bushel or $200.

Currency Futures

A currency futures contract works the same way as the futures contract between Myers and Smith. Instead of involving wheat, a currency futures contract involves a foreign currency.

For example, suppose Bill owns a Toyota dealership. It is now May, and Bill plans to buy Toyotas from Japan in August. He knows that he must buy the Toyotas with yen. He wonders what the price of yen will be in August. The current price of yen is $0.012. If the price of yen rises from $0.012 to $0.018, Bill will have to pay more for each Toyota in the shipment.

Bill enters into a futures contract with Julie. Julie agrees that in August, she will sell Bill an agreed-upon amount of yen at an exchange rate of 1 yen = $0.012.

Julie thinks the dollar price of yen will go down between now and August. If she's right and the actual exchange rate in August is 1 yen = $0.011, then she will make a profit.

Options

An **option** is a contract that gives the owner of the option the right, but not the obligation, to buy or sell shares of a stock at a specified price on or before a specified date. The specified price in an option is called the strike price. The two types of options are call options and put options.

Call Options

A call option gives the owner of the option the right to buy shares of a stock at a specified price within the time limits of the contract. For example, suppose Brown buys a call option for $20. The call option says that she can buy 100 shares of IBM stock at a strike price of $150 a share within the next month. If the price of IBM stock falls below $150 a share, Brown doesn't exercise her call option. She simply accepts the fact that she has lost $20. If the price rises above $150 a share, she exercises her call option. She buys the stock at $150 a share. Then she sells the stock for the higher market price. She makes a profit.

If Brown buys a call option, then someone must sell it to her. Any person who thinks that Brown won't exercise the option will be willing to sell it to her. Suppose Jackson believes that the price of IBM stock is going to fall below $150 a share. Then he will gladly sell a call option to Brown for $20 because he thinks that the option will not be exercised. If he's right, the sale earns him $20.

Put Options

A put option gives the owner the right, but not the obligation, to sell (rather than buy) shares of a stock at a strike price during some period of time. For example, suppose Martin buys a put option to sell 100 shares of IBM stock at $130 a share during the next month. If the share price rises above $130, Martin will not exercise his put option. He will sell the stock for more than $130 a share. On the other hand, if the price drops below $130 a share, then he will exercise his option to sell the stock for $130 a share. People who think the price of a stock is going to decline would buy a put option.

People who think the price of a stock is going to rise would sell a put option. For example, you might sell a put option for, say, $20, if you believe that the price of the stock is going to rise and the buyer of the put option is not going to exercise the option.

How You Can Use Call and Put Options

If you think the price of a stock is going to rise during the next few months, you can buy a call option. A call option will sell for a fraction of the cost of the stock. If the price of the stock does rise, you can sell your call option or you can buy the stock at the lower price specified on the call option. If you buy the stock, you can turn around and sell it at the higher current price.

If you think the price of a stock is going to fall during the next few months, you can buy a put option. Like a call option, a put option will sell for a fraction of the cost of the stock. If the price of the stock does fall, you can sell your put option to someone who wants to sell his or her stock at the higher price specified on the put option.

Answer questions 1–3 in the Section 3 Assessment on page 497 of your textbook.

Name: _____ Date: _____

CHAPTER 16
Graphic Organizer Activity

Supply the missing words in the blank spaces of these graphic organizers.

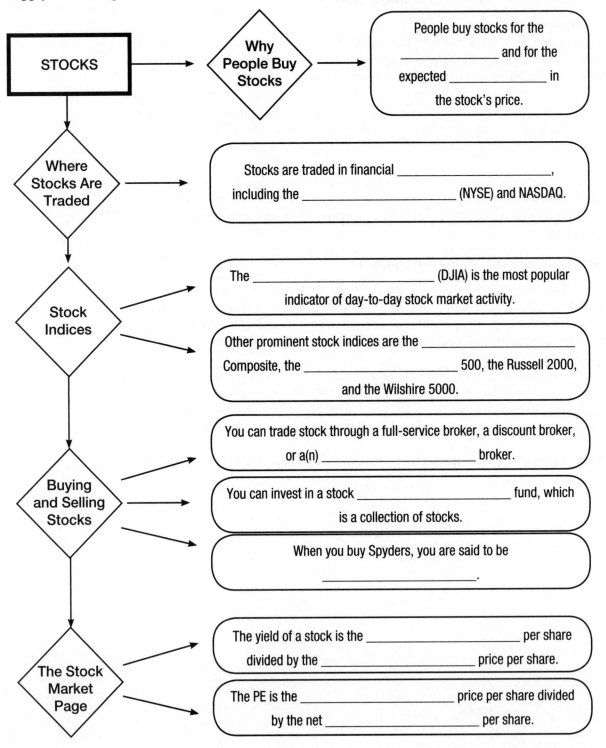

STOCKS

Why People Buy Stocks

People buy stocks for the _____ and for the expected _____ in the stock's price.

Where Stocks Are Traded

Stocks are traded in financial _____, including the _____ (NYSE) and NASDAQ.

Stock Indices

The _____ (DJIA) is the most popular indicator of day-to-day stock market activity.

Other prominent stock indices are the _____ Composite, the _____ 500, the Russell 2000, and the Wilshire 5000.

Buying and Selling Stocks

You can trade stock through a full-service broker, a discount broker, or a(n) _____ broker.

You can invest in a stock _____ fund, which is a collection of stocks.

When you buy Spyders, you are said to be _____.

The Stock Market Page

The yield of a stock is the _____ per share divided by the _____ price per share.

The PE is the _____ price per share divided by the net _____ per share.

Guided Reading and Study Guide

© EMC Publishing

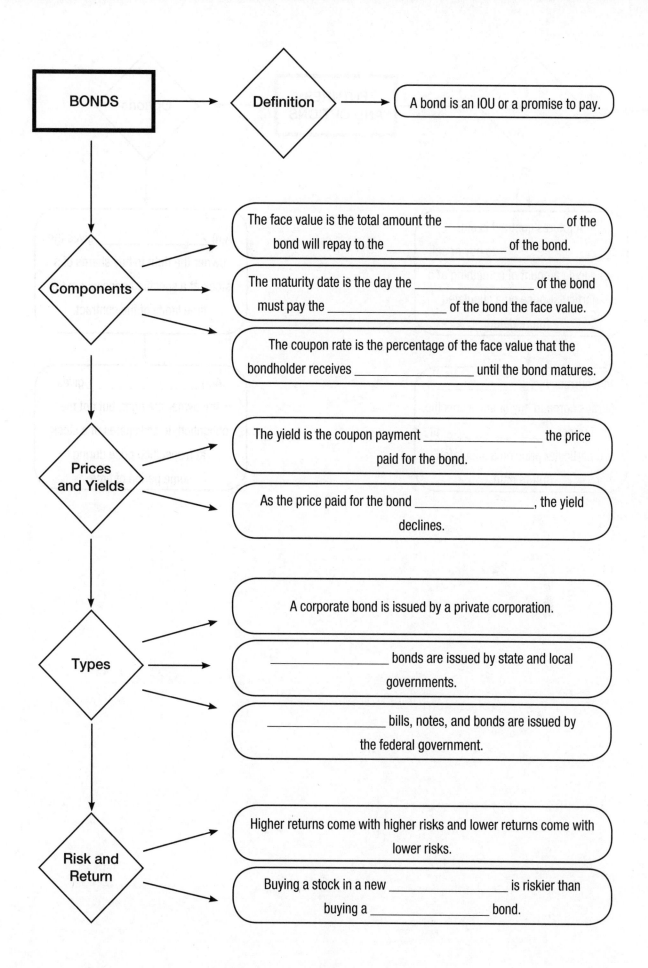

BONDS → **Definition** → A bond is an IOU or a promise to pay.

Components

The face value is the total amount the _____ of the bond will repay to the _____ of the bond.

The maturity date is the day the _____ of the bond must pay the _____ of the bond the face value.

The coupon rate is the percentage of the face value that the bondholder receives _____ until the bond matures.

Prices and Yields

The yield is the coupon payment _____ the price paid for the bond.

As the price paid for the bond _____, the yield declines.

Types

A corporate bond is issued by a private corporation.

_____ bonds are issued by state and local governments.

_____ bills, notes, and bonds are issued by the federal government.

Risk and Return

Higher returns come with higher risks and lower returns come with lower risks.

Buying a stock in a new _____ is riskier than buying a _____ bond.

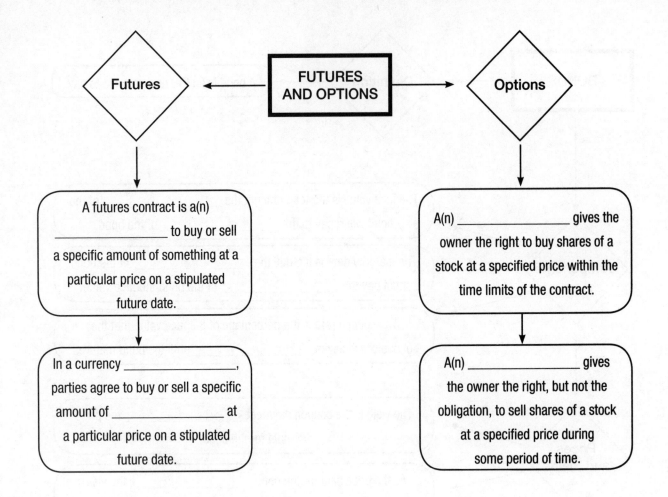

Futures

FUTURES AND OPTIONS

Options

A futures contract is a(n) _____ to buy or sell a specific amount of something at a particular price on a stipulated future date.

A(n) _____ gives the owner the right to buy shares of a stock at a specified price within the time limits of the contract.

In a currency _____, parties agree to buy or sell a specific amount of _____ at a particular price on a stipulated future date.

A(n) _____ gives the owner the right, but not the obligation, to sell shares of a stock at a specified price during some period of time.

Guided Reading and Study Guide

CHAPTER 16

Vocabulary Activity

For each question, fill in the blank with the correct term from the following list.

stock	dividend	coupon rate
Dow Jones Industrial Average (DJIA)	index	yield
initial public offering (IPO)	bond	futures contract
investment bank	face value (par value)	option

1. The _____ is equal to the annual coupon payment divided by the price paid for the bond.

2. A(n) _____ is a contract that gives the owner the right, but not the obligation, to buy or sell shares of a good at a specified price on or before a specified date.

3. A portfolio of stocks, which represents a particular market or a portion of it, used to measure changes in a market or an economy is a(n) _____.

4. The percentage of the face value that the bondholder receives each year until the bond matures is the _____.

5. A company's first offering of stock to the public is a(n) _____.

6. A(n) _____ is the share of the profits of a corporation distributed to stockholders.

7. The dollar amount specified on a bond is the _____.

8. _____ is a claim on the assets of a corporation that gives the purchaser a share of the corporation.

9. A(n) _____ is an IOU, or a promise to pay, issued by companies, governments, or government agencies for the purpose of borrowing money.

10. The _____ is the most popular, widely cited indicator of day-to-day stock market activity.

11. An agreement to buy or sell a specific amount of something (commodity, currency, financial instrument) at a particular price on a stipulated future date is a(n) _____.

12. A(n) _____ acts as an intermediary between the company that issues the stock and the public that wishes to buy the stock.

CHAPTER 16

Working with Graphs and Tables Activity

Complete the following table.

Face value of bond	Coupon rate	Coupon payment	Price paid for bond	Yield
$5,000	4%	_____	$4,800	_____
_____	7%	$700	$10,000	_____
$50,000	_____	$2,500	$50,000	_____
_____	6%	$3,000	_____	6%
$50,000	6%	_____	_____	6.25%
$50,000	6%	$3,000	$51,500	_____

CHAPTER 16

Practice Test

Multiple Choice

Circle the letter of the correct answer.

1. Which of the following is an agreement to buy or sell a specific amount of something at a particular price on a specified future date?

   a. a futures contract
   b. an option
   c. a put
   d. a bond

2. Which of the following is a reason why a person might enter into a futures contract?

   a. the person thinks a particular stock will rise in price in the future but doesn't have enough money to buy the stock itself
   b. the person thinks the share price of a stock is going to fall
   c. the person thinks the dividend will fall
   d. the person wants to lock in a price in advance

3. The annual coupon payment divided by the face value of a bond is which of the following?

   a. yield
   b. coupon rate
   c. dividend
   d. price

4. The dividend divided by the closing price of a stock is which of the following?

   a. yield
   b. coupon rate
   c. PE ratio
   d. price

5. The issuer of a bond is which of the following?

   a. buyer
   b. borrower
   c. lender
   d. saver

6. If the yield of a bond is the same as the coupon rate, which of the following is true?

   a. The coupon rate is the yield divided by the face value.
   b. The price paid for the bond is the same as the face value.
   c. The yield is the annual coupon payment divided by the face value.
   d. The face value of the bond is the yield times the price paid.

7. If the annual coupon payment is $20 and the price paid for the bond is $3,240, what will the bondholder receive in the year the bond matures?

    a. $3,220
    b. $3,260
    c. $3,240
    d. $20

8. Which of the following is a bond issued by the federal government?

    a. corporate bond
    b. Treasury option
    c. Treasury bill
    d. coupon rate

9. The rate of return that a person would receive if the person bought a bond today at its ask price and held it until it matured is which of the following?

    a. Treasury option
    b. yield
    c. Treasury bill
    d. coupon rate

10. Which of the following would you purchase if you decided to "buy the market"?

    a. dividends
    b. mutual funds
    c. Treasury bills
    d. Spyders

Short Answer

Write your answers on the lines provided.

1. Explain what the PE ratio of a stock means.

    _____

    _____

    _____

2. Explain the main components of a bond.

    _____

    _____

    _____

    _____

3. Where might a stock be sold?

_____

_____

_____

4. Give some reasons why you might want to purchase a stock.

_____

_____

_____

5. Why would a person be willing to enter into a futures contract with a corn farmer in which the person agrees to buy all the farmer's corn in two months at the current price?

_____

_____

_____